Foreword

GENETICS is the youngest branch of biology, and more papers are produced every year on genetical subjects than in any other single branch of biology with the exception of physiology.

The fast and spectacular growth of this science has had the unfortunate consequence that the majority of scientists, and even of biologists, cannot keep abreast of it; as a result of this, and also owing to the disorderly development which is inevitable at times in any young field of research, genetics has acquired the reputation of being obscure and very difficult to understand. This, however, is not the case; certain aspects of genetics are as lucid as mathematics, but much simpler. It is true that for genetical research specialized knowledge is required in one or more other branches of biology, whether zoology, botany, anthropology or clinical medicine, and some insight into statistics is also needed, but to understand the underlying principles no great accumulation of knowledge is necessary, but only a certain intellectual effort.

One drawback to the study of genetics is that it is impossible to avoid the use of a considerable number of technical terms; the number has been kept fairly low in this book, but it cannot be reduced beyond a certain minimum. To understand this terminology is in itself half the battle, and the reader is advised to use the glossary at the end of the book whenever he is not sure of the meaning of a word.

To study genetics not only provides considerable intellectual satisfaction, but the knowledge acquired is of increasing practical importance. The application of genetical principles to plant and animal breeding has already led to important economic advances, and, although the science of human genetics is at present under a cloud, owing to misunderstandings and abuse, there is no question but that it should be of ever-growing importance, and even to-day some of the decisions taken by medical practitioners are determined by genetical knowledge.

This little book was written at the instigation of Miss L. M. Crump and in collaboration with her. My chief, Professor J. B. S. Haldane, F.R.S., and my colleague Dr. Ursula Philip have read the manuscript critically and made valuable suggestions which I gratefully acknowledge; I also thank Professor L. S. Penrose who read the last two chapters, Dr. M. D. White, who has read the chapters concerning the chromosomes and corrected some errors, while Dr. R. Race has put me right in respect of the paragraphs on the Rhesus factor. The presentation of the material in Chapter III owes much to Dr. D. J. Finney's lectures. To the publishers and authors who have given me permission to use certain figures I want to express my sincere thanks; the sources of these figures are acknowledged in the captions.

HANS KALMUS

University College, London
April, 1945

Contents

GENETICS

H. KALMUS

SC.D. AND M.D. PRAGUE
DEPARTMENT OF BIOMETRY, EUGENICS AND GENETICS
UNIVERSITY COLLEGE, LONDON

in collaboration with

LETTICE M. CRUMP

M.SC. ROTHAMSTED EXPERIMENTAL STATION

PENGUIN BOOKS
HARMONDSWORTH · MIDDLESEX

FIRST PUBLISHED IN PELICAN BOOKS 1948
REPRINTED 1950

MADE AND PRINTED IN GREAT BRITAIN
FOR PENGUIN BOOKS LTD
BY RICHARD CLAY AND COMPANY LTD
BUNGAY, SUFFOLK

CHAPTER I

Introductory

GENETICS as commonly understood deals with inborn properties of organisms as distinct from the properties imposed upon them by the environment; this difference between nature and nurture was the origin of all genetical enquiry. But whereas at an earlier date it was thought that any character could be explained either by inborn or by environmental influences, it is now realized that these are not mutually exclusive and that not only is there no organism without an environment, but that each character or property of every organism is the product of numerous innate and environmental influences.

It is true that in practice characters are found which are little affected by the usual variation in external conditions—eye-colour and finger-prints in man fall into this category—but other characters, and among them many of economic importance, are very greatly influenced by the treatment their bearers receive. Even the best dairy cow will produce milk that is poor in both quantity and quality if she is underfed, and the best wheat seed will yield only a poor harvest if it is grown on sand; for although the excellence of the strains is certainly due to innate qualities, it can show only under reasonably favourable conditions. Thus any profitable analysis of the properties and performance of an organism must take into consideration both genetics and environment.

A more precise description, which is also of greater value to the working scientist, would be that genetics deals with the innate or inborn *differences* between fairly similar related organisms; such differences as there are between a black and a tabby cat, or a white rose and a red one, or a Negro and a Chinese. More distant relationships, such as those between a cat and a tiger, an apple and a pear, or a man and a chimpanzee, are not at present readily accessible to investigation by genetical methods, but they may become so in the future. In particular, genetical homologies between these and even more widely separated groups will become manifest as genetical analysis progresses.

Modern genetical theory assumes that innate differences—that is, differences developing in a uniform environment—are due to different *genes*. The genes are distinct particles of ultramicroscopic dimensions localized in the chromosomes of the cell nuclei, and as a rule they propagate themselves, or are copied at nuclear division; they are probably proteins of a particular type known as nucleo-proteins. The differences between genetically different strains are believed to result from differences arising by a sudden change, or mutation, in one or several genes; such mutations may occur during the copying process or at any other time in the nuclear cycle. Once a gene has mutated it is propagated in the altered state, provided that another mutation does not change it again; a second mutation may produce a third type of gene, or it may restore the gene to its original constitution.

The first step in any genetical investigation is therefore to prove that the difference under observation is inherited as one or several units; this is done by standardizing the environment as far as possible and then crossing the different types. The result can then be put into technical language of a rather theoretical nature by stating that strain *A* and strain *B* differ by a factor (gene) *x*, or rather that one strain is carrying a gene *x*1 and the other a gene *x*2. The gap between the experimental result and this deduction is at present wider than is usual in the other biological sciences—in fact, the theory of genes is to some extent comparable with the atomic and molecular theory shortly after its establishment. This does not mean that genes are atoms, or even molecules, although the difference between a gene and its mutant may be due to a difference of molecular structure. To fill in this gap between the gene itself and its effect on the appearance or performance of the developing organism is a further step in genetical investigation.

Genes do not occur outside an organism, and in this and in some other respects they resemble certain pathological entities, the viruses; they also have in common with the viruses their size and the fact that they are composed of nucleo-proteins and can multiply themselves indefinitely. It is clear that the biology of both genes and viruses can only be studied together with their carriers. The carriers of the mutant genes, also loosely called mutants, are thus the main objects of genetical study, and they are also the entities which are subject to natural selection and to breeding practice. Mutation—that is, the alteration of a gene—does not seem to be directly influenced by the environment, so the old ideas of direct genetical adaptation, which are now usually described as Lamarckian, are not supported by genetical evidence, and evolution seems to work by a system of trial and error in which the mutation of the genes provides Darwin's inherited variation and the environmental factors select the organisms carrying favourable gene combinations.

It is sometimes easy to distinguish between the genetically different classes in a population—for instance, between a red and a white carnation—but sometimes elaborate statistical methods are necessary to establish such differences; this is particularly true of differences in characters such as stature and weight, or the numbers of scales or bristles, which are frequently due to differences in many genes. Mathematical treatment is also necessary when the multiple combinations of many genes affecting different characters are under consideration. The study of the spreading and the equilibrium of mutant genes in populations has developed into another new branch of mathematics, and the testing of all the complicated deductions and hypotheses resulting from genetical investigations has led to the development of a new branch of statistics; this, however, can be dealt with only very superficially in this book.

Genetical theory is greatly supported in many of its aspects by cytological evidence; for example, the distribution of genes in certain crosses can be explained by the number and structure of the *chromosomes* which are supposed to carry them, and this can often be checked by direct microscopical observation. Consequently a certain knowledge of cytology is essential for the understanding of genetical evidence; the necessary cytological groundwork is provided in Chapters IX and X of this book.

CHAPTER II

What Is Inherited

SCIENCE takes its words from ordinary language, and in doing this necessarily alters their meanings to some extent; as the same thing happens, too, in other branches of knowledge, it is inevitable that very different meanings come to be attached to a word, according to the way in which it is being used and the person who is using it. The word inheritance is a case in point. In law we talk about the inheritance of money, or land, or other property, all of which can be taken away from the owner, and it is just this possibility of taking things away which makes laws about inheritance necessary; in biology, on the other hand, inheritance means the reappearance in a descendant of qualities which were present in his parents, or grandparents, or more remote forbears—such qualities as blue eyes or colour-blindness—and these are properties that cannot be taken away. These qualities show a striking discontinuity in their appearance; not only has the human ovum, sperm and young embryo no eyes the colour of which can be noted and whose vision can be found to be faulty, but the inherited characters manifest in the fully developed stage may also lapse for one or many generations only to reappear all of a sudden completely unchanged. This behaviour can best be explained by the assumption that something material is handed on through the generations which may or may not condition the development of an organism in a specific way, causing it to have, say, blue or brown eyes.

This material substrate is nowadays conceived of as particulate, and each particle is a gene; the genes are capable of reproduction, and are localized in the chromosomes, which are persistent structures found in the nuclei of all ova and sperms and of most other cells; the chromosomes can be stained with various dyes, and are then visible under the microscope. The properties of genes form one of the main subjects of this book.

In earlier times ideas about such things as inheritance were vaguer than they are now, though even nowadays there is a good deal of confused thinking, and inherited titles, for example, are regarded by some people as proving inborn nobility, although clearly they are really much more of the nature of an acquired fortune than of an innate personal quality such as colour-blindness.

A distinction has also sometimes been drawn between the inheritance of characters of what are called body, mind and soul, the soul in such cases being regarded as separately created from the body and therefore not subject to the laws of heredity; there is, however, overwhelming evidence that hereditary factors influence all spheres of life, and human temperaments, which are regarded as attributes of the soul, are associated with definite body constitutions and are known to be inherited just as much as are physical characters. The following example shows what may be inherited in the mental sphere. A normal child starts talking when it is about a year old. That this is due to inherent qualities can be seen from the fact that there are some children—idiotic children, for instance—who do not begin to talk at this stage and who may never achieve anything resembling effective language, although they have exactly the same opportunities as their fellows. But what language will a child talk if he is normal? The answer is obviously that he will always pick up the language of his parents or of the other people who care for him.

It is very interesting to speculate what sort of language a

normal child would acquire if nobody were to talk to him, and in different ages different answers have been suggested. There is a report of an English prince who many hundreds of years ago was brought up quite by himself on a remote island, and the pious chronicler reports that this boy began to talk Hebrew, this being God's language. When the same question was propounded in Egypt still earlier, another answer was given. Herodotus reports that the Egyptian king Psammetichus wanted to know whether the Egyptians were really the most ancient people; he therefore ordered two new-born babies to be isolated and not spoken to during their infancy, to see what language they would ultimately speak. To the King's annoyance, it was reported that at the age of two years the children frequently used the word 'bekos', which was interpreted as a Phrygian word for bread. From cases that come before the law courts dealing with rural crime we know nowadays that such an unfortunate isolated child develops only a very poor set of sounds, but it can quickly pick up the art of talking when it is brought into contact with speaking people, provided that it is normally gifted.

We conclude, therefore, that the faculty of talking depends upon inherited factors, but that what is talked, what language and what particular words and what grammar will be used, are determined by environment. This conclusion raises again the fundamental problem of biology—the interrelationship between heredity and environment or nature and nurture. In the case of the child learning to talk it is clear that the end-product—namely, the child speaking his parents' language—is a combined result of both inherited and environmental factors.

A striking feature of investigations into heredity is that they deal with differences rather than with similarities. If all the flowers of a species had red petals it would clearly be very difficult to see how this was brought about, but if some have white petals, and if, moreover, the colour is inherited according to definite rules, one is in a position to compare what happens in the different plants, and so to get a better insight into the development of the red colour. This principle of learning from differences is not confined to heredity; a healthy man is usually not very much interested in the functioning of his organs, but when his heart or his kidneys ail he becomes aware of the disorder, and this leads him to find out something about the order.

Observation suggests that tall parents tend to have tall children, and that parents with blue eyes tend to have children with blue eyes, and this can be established as true if measurements of the members of many families are taken; therefore there is a suspicion that being tall is at least to some extent an inherited character. Such a suspicion will be justified if the particular property appears more frequently in some families than in others, but the members of a family usually have many other things in common besides their hereditary peculiarities, such as many of the factors which constitute the environment. In a well-to-do family, for example, everybody will get more and better food than in a poor one, and this will clearly influence stature; on the other hand, we do not at present know of any means of altering a child's eye-colour. It is clear that there are inherited characters which materialize to some extent independently of the environment, whereas others lead to quite different end-results if they are exposed to favourable or unfavourable conditions.

There is another distinction which can be drawn between different inherited characters, and that is whether they divide the members of a population into sharply defined classes, such as men and women, or plants with red flowers and those with white flowers, or whether there is a continuous range such as we find between the tallest and shortest inmates of a school or in the weights of apples from a tree.

If one wants to see how heredity works it is necessary to study the offspring of individuals who differ in their inborn qualities, and if possible the study should be continued to a second and third generation. This can be done most easily by crossing individuals belonging to the same species but differing in one or two inborn characters; a red sweet pea may be pollinated with pollen from a white one, or a waltzing albino mouse may be crossed with an ordinary house mouse. It is more difficult to cross individuals belonging to different species, and it usually proves to be impossible to get offspring from the products of such a cross. Nobody knows what is the inherent difference between a horse and a donkey; it is true that offspring can be produced by crossing them in both ways—that is, from a stallion and a jenny, as well as from a jackass and a mare—but both these hybrids are as a rule sterile and cannot produce young, and so it is impossible to know what the single differences are and how they separate. Sometimes fertile offspring may come from a cross between species; the loganberry arises from a cross between a raspberry and a blackberry, and it can either be propagated directly or can be crossed back to either of the parent species.

Before going farther it should be stressed once more that it is not the visible properties of living individuals that are inherited, but rather the ability to produce distinct properties; not the red hair or the blue petal is inherited, but only the ability to produce red hair and blue petals under certain conditions, and the material entities which produce these different characters are the genes.

Similar results can sometimes be produced by genetical and environmental control; thus the poor weight of an ox may be due either to a weak genetical constitution or to malnutrition, and a bandy-legged puppy may either be descended from a dachshund or have been reared on a diet deficient in vitamin D. To take an even cruder example, fair straight hair may have grown naturally or it may have been produced by bleaching and dekinking. Sometimes the interaction of innate and environmental effects is very intricate indeed: Manx cats are a race without tails, but there is no tailless race of dogs; in practice however, the ears and tails of puppies of some breeds are clipped, and whether they are cut or not is dependent on the genetical constitution of the dog. That the offspring of such dogs are never born without tails or with markedly shortened tails might have discouraged Lamarckians from experiments in which attempts were made to produce a tailless strain of mice by cutting off their tails for many generations. A more subtle attempt to induce a genetical change by the disuse of an organ was made by breeding about seventy generations of *Drosophila melanogaster*—a small fruit-fly—in the dark, but here again the experiments failed in their aim and no visible change could be detected in the light reactions of the offspring.

CHAPTER III

Some Mathematics: Probability and Distribution

HEREDITY can only be studied in such groups as families, tribes or strains where all the members are the progeny of some common ancestry. Hereditary differences in such a progeny are distributed in accordance with simple mathematical laws, which may be directly observable in some organisms but which are usually complicated by chance distribution. Chance, in turn, is described by the rules of statistical probability, and it is necessary to understand the rudiments of this science before the significance of any factor distribution can be assessed.

If one tosses a coin it may fall with either head or tail uppermost; very rarely it may happen that it will stand on its edge, but if this possibility is ruled out heads are to be expected with about the same frequency as tails. The probability of getting heads in these circumstances is called half, or 50 per cent, and accordingly probability can be defined as relative frequency—that is, the frequency of heads divided by the frequency of tails plus heads. It is worth while to carry out such an experiment and tabulate the results; the record of an actual series of tosses is given on page 20.

From these results it is clear that, roughly speaking, the higher the number of throws the more nearly one gets to the expected result—namely, that half the throws should be heads and half tails.

To take another problem demonstrating the combination of groups of units: the probability of drawing a court card (knave, queen, king) from a well-shuffled pack of

NUMBER OF THROWS	HEADS	PERCENTAGE
1	0	0
2	0	0
3	1	33·3
5	2	40·0
10	4	40·0
20	7	35·0
50	20	40·0
100	49	49·0
200	95	47·5
500	253	50·6
1,000	504	50·4
15,000	7,457	49·9

cards is $\frac{12}{52}$, and the probability of drawing one of the numbers from 1 to 10 is $\frac{40}{52}$. As there are no cards of any other type in the pack, the probability of drawing either a court card or a number is $\frac{12}{52} + \frac{40}{52}$, which equals 1—that is, it is a certainty.

Still more can be learnt from tossing a coin if the tosses are arranged in groups; for instance, if one writes down the results of a hundred groups each consisting of ten consecutive throws, and then arranges the results according to the number of heads in each group, there will be eleven different kinds of groups. These can be arranged according to the number of times that each kind of group appears, and the result of one such experiment is given on page 21.

As one would expect, there are most cases where the numbers of heads and tails in a group are equal and fewest where there are no heads or no tails at all; further, the maximum is in the middle, and there are about equal numbers of cases in the classes which are at the same distance from the middle. The distribution is therefore a symmetrical one, and as the classes must jump by at least one—since there is no

NUMBER OF HEADS IN GROUP OF 10 THROWS	NUMBER OF CASES
0	0
1	0
2	6
3	11
4	16
5	32
6	19
7	10
8	4
9	1
10	1

class of, say, $6\frac{1}{2}$ tails—it is a symmetrical discontinuous distribution.

By casting a die we may get a discontinuous distribution which is asymmetrical, and it may interest some readers to plot in an actual experiment the number of groups of six throws containing 0–6 'ones'. The theory of such an experiment is as follows: the probability that the first throw in any group will be a 'one' is of course $\frac{1}{6}$, and the probability that all six throws will be 'ones' is $(\frac{1}{6})^6$. The probabilities of obtaining groups containing 0, 1, 2 . . . 6 'ones', or in other words their frequencies in a very large population, are then:

6 ones	$(\frac{1}{6})^6$	0·00002143
5 „	$6(\frac{1}{6})^5 . \frac{5}{6}$	0·00064300
4 „	$15(\frac{1}{6})^4 . (\frac{5}{6})^2$	0·00803755
3 „	$20(\frac{1}{6})^3 . (\frac{5}{6})^3$	0·05358368
2 „	$15(\frac{1}{6})^2 . (\frac{5}{6})^4$	0·20093879
1 „	$6(\frac{1}{6}) . (\frac{5}{6})^5$	0·40187757
0 „	$(\frac{5}{6})^6$	0·33489798
		1·00000000

Thus among 100,000 groups of six throws there would be on the average only two where six 'ones' are thrown, 40·188 groups would contain a single 'one' and 33·490 no 'ones' at all. Figure 1 gives the histogram of this skew distribution, while an example of an actual skew distribution (human weights) is given in Figure 4.

So far we have dealt with distinct classes only, but continuous properties can also be arranged in classes which are then artificial; it is convenient to plot the numbers on a

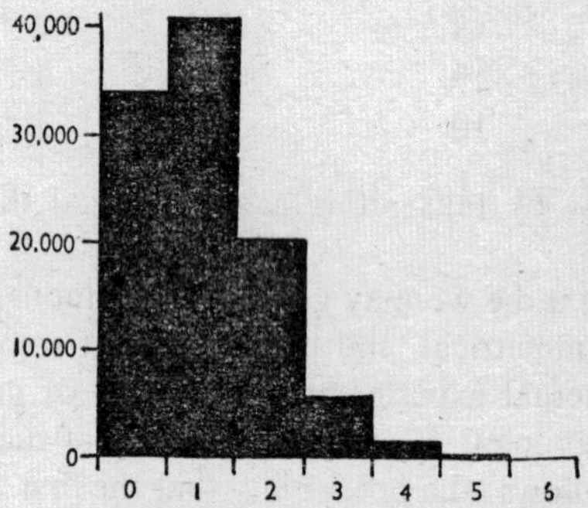

FIG. 1.—Distribution of 100,000 groups of six throws containing 0–6 'ones'.

curve—for instance, the numbers of schoolboys in a big town can be plotted against their ages. Such a diagram is given in Figure 2.

From this graph it is obvious that there are no schoolboys under three years old and none over nineteen, and the most common age is about seven. There are roughly equal numbers of boys above and below ten years, and this value is called the *median*. The mean age of all the boys, however, is eleven years. If the curve in the graph is copied on a piece of cardboard and cut out, it is found that when the figure is supported with the twelve-year mark on the edge of a knife it is in equilibrium. If one wants to know what is the probability that the age of any boy taken at random lies between fifteen and sixteen years, one has to compare the frequency of boys between these two ages with the frequency of all the boys. These frequencies are indicated not only by the numbers of the boys, but also by the relative sizes of the area between fifteen and sixteen and the total area taking the latter as unity. This becomes important when continuous distributions are investigated. To save the complicated geo-

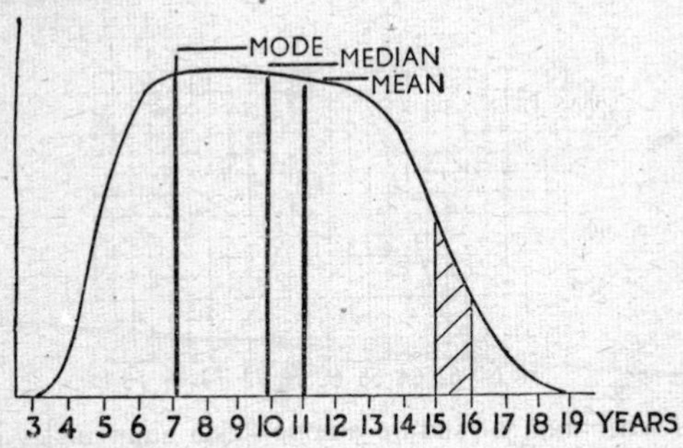

FIG. 2.—Distribution of ages of schoolboys in a large town. The probability that the age of any boy taken at random is between 15 and 16 years is obtained from the ratio between the shaded area and the total area; the total area is usually taken to be 1.

metrical labour of determining the areas of such curves, mathematical tables exist where these values can be found.

We have now dealt with discrete symmetrical and asymmetrical distributions and with an asymmetrical (skew) continuous distribution; the most important type, however, as far as biology and genetics are concerned, is a special case of symmetrical continuous distribution, known as a normal or Gaussian distribution, after a German mathematician whose name was Gauss. He applied it originally to the arrangement of errors occurring in physical measurements;

its shape is given in Figure 3, which shows the frequencies of different statures among British men. The most common case, the median case and the mean case, are identical in this normal distribution, instead of occurring at different values, which makes calculating much easier. There are other mathematical properties of this curve that make it very convenient to use.

If samples of great masses of natural objects are taken—for instance, the weights of the fruits of a certain plant, or the heights of plants of the same age of a given species, or

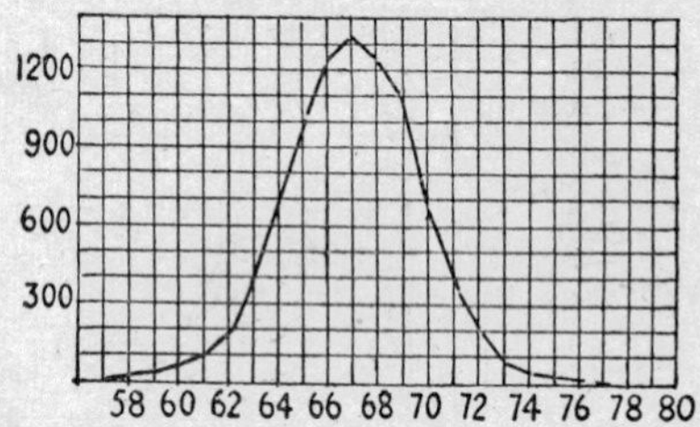

FIG. 3.—Distribution of stature among 8,585 adult males in Great Britain (1883). The values of the abscissae correspond to the beginnings of the class intervals. (After Kendall, 1943.)

the wing areas of individuals of any insect species—the single measurements will frequently be found to be arranged roughly in a normal distribution. If they are not, suspicion is justified that the material under consideration is not homogeneous; for example, it might consist of fruits of hybrids from two plant races, or seedlings of different plants, or a mixture of flies of different constitution. Frequently a bimodal distribution is due to the presence of two different age groups in the material. In all such cases one says that the sample has not been taken from one population.

The symmetry and shape of a distribution curve are dependent upon the entity measured: thus the size of a man can be measured either by taking his height or by weighing him. If the distribution of statures in a population is fairly normal, as in fact it is shown to be in Figure 3, the distribution of weights cannot be expected to be so too, for the bulk of a man must vary roughly with the third power of any of his linear measurements. Figure 4 shows, indeed, that the weight distribution of a population similar to the one referred to in Figure 3 is asymmetrical or skew. For mathematical reasons

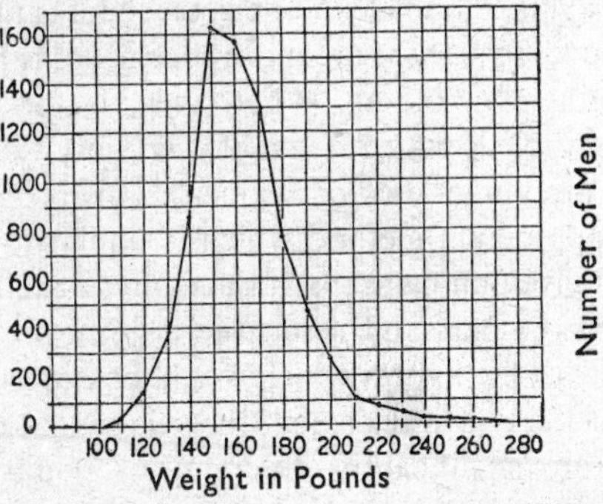

FIG. 4.—Distribution of weight in pounds among 7,749 males in the United Kingdom. (Figures from Kendall, 1943.)

it is always advantageous, if possible, to select for measuring the entity that shows the closest approximation to normality.

In genetics, as in other biological sciences, it is often essential to find out whether two groups of measurements are really different; this question may be put in the form: Do they or do they not come from the same population? This again is only a special case of an even more general statistical problem—namely, whether certain experimental data agree or disagree with an hypothesis, or whether they agree better with one assumption than with another. The mathematics needed to test such problems are often difficult, but two simple genetical examples may give some idea of the methods used. As will be shown later, the sex ratio in man is approximately but not exactly one to one, for in most populations there are more women than men; the question is, how big must the sample of a population be to make us quite confident that there are really more females in the whole population? Nobody would trust a result which took into account only the passengers in a railway carriage, as it is obvious that at different times of day there will sometimes be more men travelling and sometimes more women. Not even in an average home can one get a significant result, for, as everyone knows, there are more sons in some families and more daughters in others. What, then, is the number required to establish with reasonable certainty that there is a numerical preponderance of women? This problem can be solved by applying a method which is similar to the tossing experiment given on page 19. If the figures actually obtained by counting the men and women in a given population are compared with the figures which would be expected were the numbers of the two sexes equal, they show that the two sets of figures are significantly different. As counting is continued the proportion of men to women will not get closer to 50 : 50, but will approach more closely towards another value—for instance, 47 per cent men to 53 per cent women—and when the change in percentage becomes very small as the counts accumulate one can be confident that one is in the neighbourhood of the true value. Moreover, the significance of such a result can be measured; it is then expressed by the likelihood or probability that it is due merely to the chances of sampling. The argument here runs something as follows: if one takes only two people as the sample, it is obvious that either one gets two men, or two women, or one man and one woman, and the chances of getting either two men or two women are about 25 per cent each, while the chances of getting a mixed pair are about 50 per cent. As in such a sample merely by chance only women occur in a quarter of all cases, the result cannot support the hypothesis that there are more women than men in the population as a whole. On the other hand, if one were to count 200 females in succession, the suspicion would arise that the sample had been taken in a nunnery, or a girls' school, or some similar place, for such a result would occur in a mixed population only once in 2^{200} times, or approximately once in 10^{60} times, and the counting would involve far more people than there are living on earth (about 2×10^{9}) or than have ever lived there. This probability is so small that it can be neglected, and therefore it is quite certain that one will never get a sample of 200 women from a population made up of approximately equal numbers of both sexes. But to revert to the question of the sex ratio. If a sample properly taken from an unselected group gives, for instance, 110 women and 90 men, does this really prove that there are more females than males in the entire population?

Calculations too technical to be explained here show that it does not, for such a bad approximation to the 100 : 100 ratio, or indeed an even worse one, can be expected in about a third of many counts simply by chance. A significant result could, however, be obtained from an unselected sample of 2,000 people. The probability of getting 1,100 women in a sample of this size, provided that it is taken from a population composed of equal numbers of men and women, would be less than 1 in 1,000; hence it could be inferred that there were really more women in that population. A different and slightly more complicated problem would be to find out how well this result agreed with the assumption of any particular degree of female preponderance.

The probability of a result occurring by chance is thus indicative of its significance; the value can be chosen arbitrarily. For instance, it may be considered that a result agrees with the hypothesis if the probability that it does so purely by chance is less than 1 per cent, or less than one in a million. For most practical purposes, and especially in genetics, a result which occurred by chance not more frequently than once in twenty cases would generally be regarded as significant.

A common genetical problem is to find whether two characters are associated or not; for example, whether fair people are more likely than dark people to have light eyes, and whether dark-haired people have a greater chance of having dark eyes than fair people. It is generally assumed that both these statements are true. Leaving out of account the difficulties of classifying hair- and eye-colour which are encountered in reality, one might get the following distribution: among 100 people there might be sixty-three fair ones, among whom fifty-two had light eyes and eleven dark eyes, and thirty-seven dark people, among whom thirty had dark eyes and seven light eyes. Would such a sample prove the truth of the general assumption? To test this it is convenient to arrange the figures in the following way:—

OBSERVED VALUES

EYES	FAIR HAIR	DARK HAIR	TOTAL
Light eyes .	52	7	59
Dark eyes .	11	30	41
Total . .	63	37	100

assuming that hair- and eye-colour occur independently of each other in any of the individuals among these 100 people the following figures would be expected:—

EXPECTED VALUES

EYES	FAIR HAIR	DARK HAIR	TOTAL
Light eyes .	37·17	21·83	59
Dark eyes .	25·83	15·17	41
Total . .	63·00	37·00	100

These two results cannot be reconciled, for three times more light-eyed, dark-haired people would have been expected than actually occurred. Calculations which cannot be explained here show that such a difference between observed and expected numbers would occur by chance only once in 1,000 times, and therefore the general assumption that light hair and light eyes usually go together, and dark hair and dark eyes, appears to be correct.

CHAPTER IV

The Arrangement of Things and the Causes of their Variation

AT some future date the chemistry of genes may become the chief subject of genetical research; at present, however, the study of heredity is best begun by considering gene effects in the adult and the developing organism. It has already been said that this is most easily done by observing the differences between organisms, and the next task will be to find out (1) by what properties natural objects differ, (2) how they can be arranged in accordance with those differences, and (3) what are the causes of their variation.

Scientists have always felt impelled to put order into the things and the events which surround them. This has been especially true when new methods have led to the accumulation of large bodies of newly acquired facts. For instance, the periodic system of elements was the outcome of a century's rapid increase in chemical knowledge. About 200 years ago minerals, plants and animals were arranged in groups by the great Swedish naturalist Linnæus in a work called *Systema Naturæ*, and this book formed the basis for modern systematics. It will be useful, however, before discussing the systematic arrangements of animals and plants that have been arrived at by biologists, to have some idea of how things in general can be arranged.

During a fine night a few very bright stars can be seen in the sky; they are the larger planets, such as Venus, Mars and Jupiter. Others, the fixed stars, are more numerous and less bright, while still others can only just be seen. Among these are the smaller stars in the constellations of the Plough and the Pleiades. With a field-glass still more stars become visible, and the number increases when a powerful telescope is used, or when photographs are taken with the great reflectors. The biggest of these reflectors is now being made for the observatory of Mount Palomar in California. It is possible to arrange, let us say, 1,000 stars in order, beginning from fairly bright fixed stars, but not from Sirius or any of the other very bright ones, and proceeding to those that are just photographable in such a way that number 2 is just a little less bright than number 1, number 3 less bright than number 2 and so on to number 1,000. In this way we get a series of fixed stars ranging from bright ones to faint ones where the difference between any two neighbouring stars is very slight and the brightness decreases gradually; the series is almost *continuous*. The decrease in brightness can be made even more gradual if 10,000 stars are arranged between the same two limits. Astronomers have classified all fixed stars according to their brightness, and have set up about twenty classes, of which the first six or seven are visible without the help of instruments. As the brightness decreases continually, it is clear that these classes must be arbitrary; actually they are chosen for the convenience of the astronomers.

Many things on earth can also be arranged in continuous series: pebbles or bits of chocolate can be arranged in order according to their weights, sounds according to their pitch, light according to its colour, vessels of water according to temperature, and innumerable other things according to some quality or other. But some things cannot be arranged continuously, especially those that are connected with numbers. The whole numbers 1, 2, 3, 4, . . . and so on always jump by one, and do not merge gradually into each other; thus between 6 and 7 or between 1,008 and 1,009 there are no whole numbers. Again if we try to arrange crystals in order, we find none with, let us say, 11·37 faces; a crystal must always have a whole number of faces, edges or corners. Further, not all the crystals which are geometrically conceivable occur in nature—there are no pyramids or slopes consisting of five, seven, nine, ten or eleven faces all of which are equal. Altogether the study of crystals shows that only thirty-two classes are possible, and these are usually arranged in seven orders, but some of these classes have so far only been found in laboratory products. Therefore, although combinations of individual crystals exist, they can all be arranged in a definite number of natural classes according to their symmetry: the arrangement is of necessity *discontinuous*. However, some transitional forms occur in minerals, as can be seen in the angles between the axes of crystals of minerals of similar chemical composition; an example of this is found in felspar.

The periodic system of chemical elements is very strikingly discontinuous; there are ninety-two elements, possibly a few more, most of them known, and between any two of them there are no others. Thus between hydrogen and helium there are no pure gases, and there are no pure metals between gold and mercury. Here again modern physics has shown that there may be whole groups of more or less similar elements forming what was formerly regarded as one element, but even these isotopes are clearly separated.

Discontinuous arrangements are also found among manufactured goods, although it is not of necessity so. There are perhaps four or five sizes of spoons or forks with no intermediate sizes in between, milk-bottles are normally produced only in a few sizes, and so on. But if the volumes of pint milk-bottles were very accurately measured a certain variability would appear; the distribution around the pint size would be continuous, but there would be a jump from the pint to the quart size. The measurements of living things also cluster round certain average values; the weights of the eggs, or the wing areas or the leaf areas of members of a species may vary within narrow limits, whereas the same measurements made on members of a related species may be quite distinct, though in many cases there will be considerable overlapping.

Often the same things can be so ordered as to give either a continuous or a discontinuous arrangement, depending on the principle upon which the order is based. Thus it would be possible to arrange a fairly continuous series of all living organisms according to their weights, although such a system would have only a very limited utility, as a crayfish and a tulip could easily become neighbours, and could readily change places if a greater crayfish were substituted for a smaller one. Other criteria than weight are generally used for arranging animals and plants in order, such as their build or their habitations, or their utility to mankind.

Manifoldness is an outstanding feature of living things, though this also applied to man-made things before modern industry brought about standardization. It is almost impossible to find two leaves on an oak tree which cannot be distinguished from one another, though they are all of them obviously oak leaves and are easily distinguishable from maple leaves. The branch of biology which occupies itself with arranging living objects in a discontinuous way according to their structure is called systematics. When such a method is applied we find first large groups, such as birds and insects, mosses and algæ, and very little in between to link them together. Inside these groups we can find smaller but also quite distinct groups, such as owls or song-birds among the birds, and beetles and dragon-flies among insects; but there are also groups of organisms, species, which seem to be capable of continuous or even of reticulate arrangements and which are grouped differently by different specialists. Thus in the Iceland poppy various species of the genus may differ in petal colour, growth, arrangement of the leaves and other characters in such a way that species which are alike in one character differ in others, so that it is impossible to arrive at a linear arrangement, and different groupings result according to which character is taken as a criterion.

The same thing is found if attempts are made to correlate anthropometric characters—for instance, the pigmentation of skin, hair and eyes with the shape of the skull or with stature. There is hardly any correlation between long-headedness and hair-colour, or between eye-colour and weight. Such results show the futility of trying to establish the existence of any pure human races. Characters of this type are best dealt with by the biometrician, who applies complicated mathematical methods to the study of small but measurable differences.

The most important and at the same time the most disputed unit of the systematist is the species, but as the specific characters in various groups of organisms, such as bacteria or insects or mammals, must be very different, the species definition of a systematist will vary according to his material. Nevertheless generally the species is regarded as being a more real entity than the larger systematic units, such as the genus, family or class; it may be defined as a group of organisms interbreeding, or capable of interbreeding, which form a continuous population in the statistical sense. At the same time generic and family differences probably have originated as species differences.

As it is impossible in a book like this to deal in full with the species problem, the numerous exceptions to this definition will not be discussed here, nor can the difference in approach which is found between the curator of a museum and a breeder be explained in detail.

The species of mosquitoes or ants or bacteria, and indeed of many other organisms, are arranged rather differently by different biologists, which suggests that there are no very obvious 'natural classes'. Sometimes two species are quite clearly different, but in other cases differences can be established only by elaborate measurements, or perhaps only by differences in biology. Among the individuals of a species there is always a certain amount of variation. If a large number of plants or animals of the same species are arranged according to a criterion which can be measured, such as

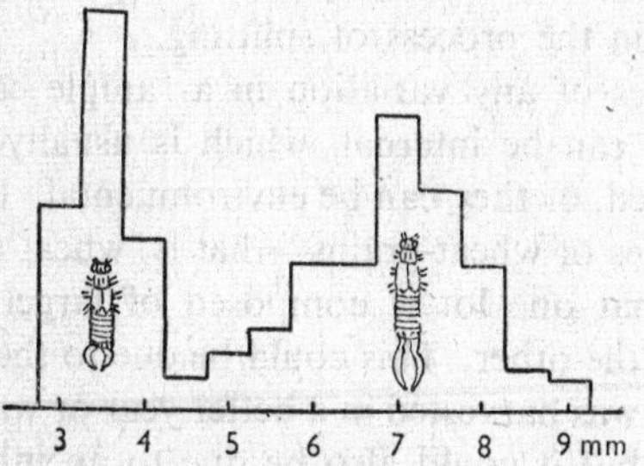

FIG. 5.—Length of pincers in millimetres of a population of earwigs. (After Babcock and Clausen, 1927.)

length and weight, or which can be counted, like the numbers of bristles or scales, the numbers obtained for the different classes of size and number will often be found to be arranged according to the normal distribution which is described on page 23. If they are not, but if instead, for example, there are two or more classes of maximum numbers separated by one or several classes of lower numbers, one says that the population in question is not a homogeneous one but a mixed (polymorphic) one of two different populations—for instance, in Figure 5 the lengths of the pincers of a sample of earwigs are shown and two maxima occur. However, before a result like this is considered to prove genetical polymorphism other possibilities must be excluded, as a similar result may be given by a mixture of individuals of two and of three years of age, or perhaps of individuals belonging to two species which appear only slightly different but are nevertheless genetically separate. The various forms in polymorphic species, such as lighter and darker forms of butterflies, or ladybirds showing different numbers of spots, may occur either simultaneously or in succession, either at the same locality or in different regions. Polymorphism in a species is often easily detectable, but in most cases it is probably more hidden. Polymorphic species are often but not always in the process of splitting.

The causes of any variation in a sample can be of two kinds: they can be internal, which is usually synonymous with inherited, or they can be environmental. If we measure dried samples of wheat-grains—that is, wheat embryos—we may find that one lot is composed of larger and heavier grains than the other. This could be due to the fact that the first sample was harvested in a better year or was grown on a better soil, but it could also be due to an inborn superior quality of the wheat from which the sample came. If we want to find out which is the true reason, it is necessary to grow wheat from both lots on the same soil and at the same time, or preferably to grow both lots on several kinds of soils. Such experiments may yield various results. It may be found, for instance, that one strain gives a heavier crop on all the soils tested, but it may also happen that one strain is more successful on some soils while the other does better on others. From this we may conclude that there may be little sense in saying that one strain is superior to another. What is needed before a complete statement can be made is a good description of the conditions in which the organism develops; the difference—that is, the superiority of one of the strains—appears only under certain defined conditions.

Any investigator will, of course, try to eliminate from his study the most obvious disturbing factors. It would be of little value to measure the stature of all the inhabitants of one town and compare it with the stature of the people of another town or of a rural district without a full knowledge of all the facts; clearly we should get a lower average in a place with more children, and if the age distribution of the two populations were not known we should arrive at quite erroneous conclusions. Further, men are taller on the average than women, and members of the richer classes tend to be taller than poorer people, so comparison of stature can only be of value where great numbers of measurements are available of people of approximately the same age, sex and social standing; unless of course it is the effect of age or sex or social standing that is being investigated. Such measurements are available in almost all civilized countries for recruits, who are usually men of about twenty years old. A study of these figures shows that in most European countries stature has increased during the last eighty years by about one centimetre per decade. The Japanese living in California are from two to three inches taller than their parents who emigrated as adults from Japan, which is clearly a result of the better living conditions in the New World, especially better food and housing.

Some critics have rightly pointed out that good food and housing do indeed speed up human growth but that the final stature attained by underfed and badly housed people may not be as inferior as is commonly believed, although it is reached later. At the present there are not enough measurements available of 'adults' to decide this difference of opinion.

Food, housing, climate, composition of the soil and similar factors constitute the environment of the organism, or what has been called its nurture. Examples of nurture exerting an influence on the measurable properties of plants and animals can easily be found. Clearly plants that do not get enough water, or animals which do not get enough food, or children who are continually exposed to infection do not grow as well as their fellows living under more favourable conditions. But there are limits to the influence of the environment in both directions—an insect, however well fed it may be, will never develop to the size of a whale, and, on the other hand, while complete lack of food may finally kill a chicken, it will never produce a grown-up hen of miniature size.

Sometimes it is difficult to decide whether variability is due to internal or to external factors. In our earwig population with two maxima of pincer size for which there is no conceivable external reason there is a strong suspicion that we are dealing with individuals which differ genetically. Very often a measurable or countable character, such as size or pigmentation or the number of cuticular appendages, is determined by many genetical factors; this is known as polygenic control. In this case we get a distribution which is normal in shape and which cannot be distinguished by mathematical methods from variation which is due to the environmental conditions. Actually most normal distributions are due to both causes, though in differing degrees; this means that even in good experimental conditions there is often a variation owing to the action of slightly different environment on slightly different constitution.

The method of distinguishing between a variation that is genetically determined and one that is due to environmental factors is the selection experiment. If a population is bred from in two directions, always pairing the largest individuals on the one hand and the smallest on the other, very different results are arrived at after several generations, according to the original genetic constitution. If the original material was a clone or a pure line, the offspring of the large and of the small individuals will not differ from each other in their average size or in the range of variation; nor will they differ from their ancestors when they are reared under similar conditions. Clearly the variation of individuals in a clone or a pure line (see page 43) is entirely due to variation in the environment. If the same process of selection is applied to a wild population the result is quite different; it is usually possible in a few generations to select strains which differ significantly in size or in other measurable characters, and this effect can be increased, sometimes

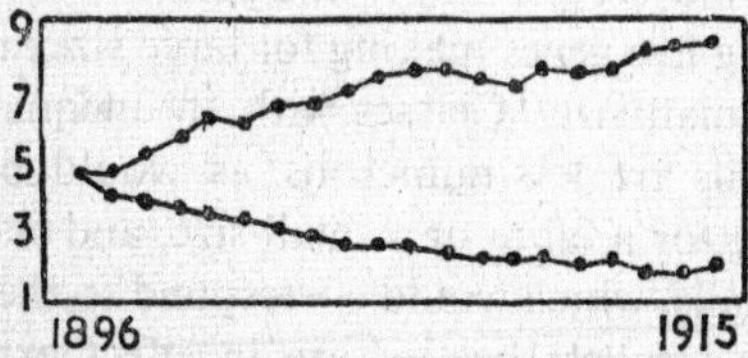

FIG. 6.—Result of 20 years' selection for high (upper line) and low (lower line) oil content in maize. (After Babcock and Clausen, 1927.)

through many generations. By this process two populations which contain different size-determining genes are being separated, one group with a majority of genes determining greater size and another group containing more equivalent genes (alleles) (see page 51) determining smaller size. This kind of selection is practised by the plant- and animal-breeder, and can be applied to many economic properties, such as the volume or the fat content of milk, the number of grains in a wheat-ear or the hardiness of bees. Figure 6 shows the effect of an experiment of this kind carried out on maize in the Illinois State corn experiments selecting for low and high oil content.

Size is one of the characters that is commonly due to the action of many genes. If we assumed that the length of a beetle were determined by ten pairs of genes, localized in ten different chromosomes, each increasing or decreasing the size of the beetle by a certain length according to its presence or absence, this extremely simplified model would give us a normal distribution of sizes in a population composed of individuals which were the outcome of a free combination of all these factors. In the penny-tossing experiment described on page 20, when groups of ten throws showing a certain proportion of heads and tails were counted, the greatest frequency was found in the class made up of five heads and five tails; this would correspond in the present case to the individuals having five genes making for large size and five genes making for small size. Classes with an unequal number of heads and tails are less numerous, as would be classes of genes making for a large or a small size, and classes with all heads or all tails, which would correspond to the very largest and the very smallest beetles, are in effect extremely rare, though they do occur.

Selection from genetically heterogeneous material is probably the most important evolutionary process in nature, and it is certainly the one that is most used in animal- and plant-breeding. It has not always been applied consciously, as it is in the development of race-horses or of fancy breeds of plants and birds, but in early times was used quite unconsciously; for instance, there was a natural tendency to breed from domestic animals which were either earlier in maturing or more prolific, even if these properties would have been counterbalanced in wild life by other factors. One is on the whole more likely to start breeding from a pig which is the offspring of a sow that matured in one year than from one that did not mature for two years, as there are a greater number of the former to choose from. Similarly the chances that an egg from which one breeds has been laid by a hen laying a great number of eggs are greater than the chances that it is the product of a poor layer. In this way early maturity and greater fertility have been unconsciously selected through many generations. A similar process can be observed in the selection of crop plants. Modern races of wheat would stand little chance of survival if cultivation stopped. It has been observed that wheat is almost absent from a furrow where it has been grown in the previous year, but under artificial conditions of agriculture the strains which produce the most grain are clearly the most likely to propagate, and as the number and size of the grains which are produced by a wheat plant happen also to determine its value to the farmer, this process of selection has been going on through the ages. Considerable increases in yield had been produced long before scientific plant-breeding began.

Of course there are also limits to selection for a character that is determined by many genes. These are reached when a homogeneous stock has been produced. However, further advance in the same direction may very occasionally occur by a sudden change of one gene. This has actually happened in the fruit-fly *Drosophila melanogaster*, where, after a slight darkening effect had been produced which could not be increased by further selection, a very dark body-colour mutant known as ebony suddenly appeared.

If further selection is desirable in a species, two strains on which selection has become ineffective can be crossed; among the offspring resulting from the recombination of the many genes by which these strains may differ some may be of greater economic value than their parent types, and may also be capable of further improvement by selection.

We have shown in this chapter how the diversity of genes forms the raw material for selection, while in another chapter we shall describe how a gene has the property of reproducing its like unless an accident occurs. Clearly it is only by accidents that diversity of genes originates, or at least it is the only known way in which it can happen. These accidents, or mutations, will be dealt with in a later chapter.

CHAPTER V

Clones, Pure Lines, Races and Strains

ORGANISMS propagate in different ways. Bacteria, as well as many organisms that consist of one cell and one nucleus, often divide into two bits. When these are of equal size this process is called binary fission; when they are unequal it is called budding. The qualities of all the descendants of such single cells are very similar, and one assumes that the genetic factors, the majority of which are probably localized in the nuclei, are evenly distributed between the two halves of the cell at each division. The descendants of a single cell reared in the laboratory under controlled conditions are therefore of a very uniform quality, and they constitute what is called a clone. All the individuals of one coral reef may also have been produced vegetatively from one pelagic larva, and thus be genetically uniform, as are also some parthenogenetic lines of water-fleas (Cladocera) and Aphids and some plants which have lost their power of sexual reproduction. However, there are other cases of parthenogenesis—for instance, among the Orthoptera—which do not result in genetically uniform progeny. Polyembryony also provides genetically homogeneous material in such widely separated forms as Miastor (Diptera) and man (monozygotic twins, triplets, etc.).

Among flowering plants many species are propagated vegetatively; strawberries are usually grown from runners, bananas do not normally contain any seeds and one plant is derived from another by taking cuttings; the grafts that give rise to the fruit-bearing parts of our apple trees are themselves bits of older trees. In this way more than 6,000,000

Cox's orange pippin trees have all been produced vegetatively from one tree which grew near Slough at the beginning of the nineteenth century; they are all uniform in their quality, whereas seedlings produced by these trees are different and variable. Some of the better-known potato varieties, such as King Edward, which are propagated by tubers, behave similarly. All such stocks which are produced by taking parts from an old plant make up a clone. A clone can therefore be defined as a population composed of individuals all descended from one single organism by vegetative propagation involving mitotic cell division only, and any variation occurring among the individuals of a clone must be due either to environmental factors, as is explained on page 36, or to changes (mutation) in the gene constitution occurring after the separation.

In most of the unicellular organisms, and in the majority of the multicellular ones, a more complicated sort of propagation occurs in addition to simple cell division. In animals a small cell—the sperm—enters a large cell—the ovum—and from these two together a new individual develops. In plants, too, similar processes can be observed. Sperms and ova can be produced by one and the same individual, as they are in the garden snail, or by different individuals, as they are in the herring; a garden snail is always a hermaphrodite, but almost all herrings are either male or female. If mice are inbred for thirty generations by mating daughters to fathers or sons to mothers they become genetically homogeneous; using brother–sister matings, more generations—about fifty to sixty—are needed to produce homogeneity. Such really pure lines have been produced in a few animals only: in mice, rats, guinea-pigs, poultry and some flies. Theoretically it is possible to say how many generations of inbreeding are needed in any species to produce a pure line leaving mutations out of account; it depends on the amount of crossing over taking place between homologous chromosomes, or, in other words, on the length of the chromosome maps (see page 80).

In all other animals 'pure line' at present only means a strain of some purity. To test the homogeneity of such a strain it is necessary to perform selection experiments (see page 38); if the stock is anywhere near purity, selection in any particular direction—say for size, height or colour—will not succeed. Thus it appears that statements as to purity, whether plants or animals are concerned, are of very different degrees of reliability. In practice the gardener or agriculturalist is usually contented with the label on his seed-packet, whereas the animal fancier or cattle-breeder always demands a pedigree. Genetically homogeneous material may also be produced by crossing the members of two pure lines. Apart from mutation the first generation of such crosses is equivalent to a clone. Such a practice is sometimes used in poultry-breeding—for instance, when Light Sussex and Rhode Island Reds are crossed.

A very important term which was originally used in systematics is 'race'. Nowadays, however, its use is avoided as far as possible in genetics. One frequently reads or hears about the human race. This clearly means the human species and comprises all mankind. One may also talk about the so-called great human races: the white, yellow, black and red. Here 'race' obviously means great divisions of humanity in which it is assumed that the members of any one group are more nearly related to each other than they are to the members of the other groups, and that the people within one group are all of a fairly similar genetical constitution. If we dealt with mankind as we do with animals or plants, we should probably describe these great groups as geographical varieties. Unfortunately the word 'race' has been made use of to discriminate among people differing in almost any respect, quite regardless of whether the differences are genetical or not; they may often be linguistic, economic or religious. To talk about the Aryan race, for example, is a misnomer, as Aryan is a term which was used at one time to describe most of the European and some of the Indian languages, and now has an even more restricted meaning. To talk of a Jewish race is at least an exaggeration, as, in spite of the differences between Jews and Gentiles in any particular country, the genetical make-up of the Jews always resembles that of the other people exposed to the same environment, and differs between Jews from country to country. It is obvious that the differences between Jews and Gentiles are to a great extent due to differences in religion or in family traditions and to other historical reasons of various kinds.

In animal and plant husbandry the word race frequently means variety; it is applied to groups of dogs, such as Terriers or Alsatians, or to vegetables—sugar peas, cauliflowers, etc.—which have been to some extent inbred. Usually some description is given of one or several characters distinguishing a particular race from the rest of the species—for instance, Japanese waltzing mice, which run after their tails, suffer from an abnormality of the inner ear, race-horses are of a lighter build than cart-horses, and red cabbages have red leaves and not green ones. Breeders of the old school rarely distinguish between the characters which are due to single gene differences and those which are due to many, and their use of the word race still remains rather vague. The term used by modern geneticists to take the place of race is strain, which has a more precise meaning; it is applied to forms which differ from the commonly found wild type by one or several precisely defined hereditary characters which usually breed true. For instance, there may be a strain of white sweet peas, or of peaches without hairs (nectarines), or of sheep without horns.

CHAPTER VI

Life Cycles and Mendelism in Haploids

WHEN a sperm and an ovum fuse, the chromosomes of both become visible and pair together, and after they have gone through the changes which are dealt with in Chapter X they form the fertilized egg or zygote from which all the cells of the new organism are descended. Let us assume that the number of chromosomes in a species is three, and let us further assume that the sperm and the egg each bring in three chromosomes; there would then be six chromosomes in the zygote. If the number of the chromosomes in the eggs and sperms which were ultimately produced by this zygote were also six, we should clearly get twelve chromosomes in the next generation, twenty-four in the generation after that, and so on. Weismann, who was one of the great biologists of the post-Darwinian era, realized that this could not go on indefinitely, and postulated the existence of a mechanism reducing the number of chromosomes, although he had not observed the actual process. This was found by various observers a generation later. There are, however, occasional lapses in the reduction process, especially in plants, which give rise to new varieties, like the varieties of blackberries. The reduction in the numbers of chromosomes takes place at several different phases in the propagation cycle of the species (Figure 7); in some primitive algæ, for instance, it occurs immediately after the egg has been fertilized, and the young plant has only half as many chromosomes as the zygote. Such a plant is called haploid, as it has only a single set of chromosomes—in our case three—whereas the nucleus of the zygote is called diploid because it has the double number, or two complete sets. In higher animals, on the other hand, the reduction of the chromosome number takes place before the zygote is actually formed, or more or less simultaneously with its formation; thus it always occurs during the formation of the sperms. But in the egg it usually does not happen until after the sperm has entered it. Therefore most animals are diploid throughout their lives, but the sperm is haploid, while the egg is not.

There are some groups of plants where the reduction of the chromosome number takes place about midway between

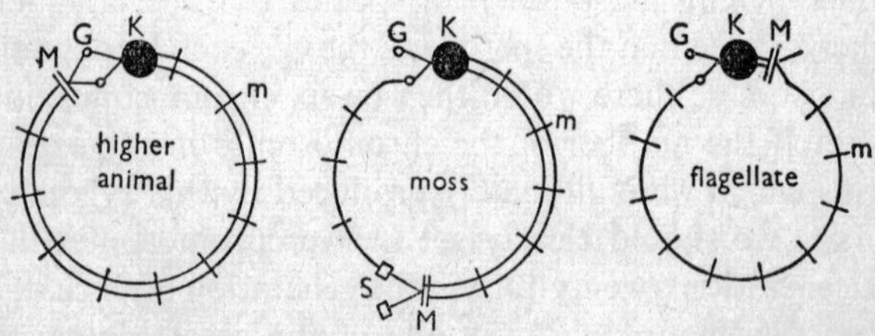

FIG. 7.—Haploid (single line) and diploid (double line) phases in three life cycles. M = meiosis (reduction from diploid to haploid), G = gamete, K = karyogamy (union of nuclei of two gametes), *m* = mitosis (cell division), *s* = spores. All schemes to be read clockwise. (After Claus, Grobben and Kühn.)

the formation of two generations of zygotes. The career of these species is therefore subdivided into two phases of about equal length, one of which is spent in the haploid and the other in the diploid state. In some algæ these two stages do not differ greatly in their external appearance or in the locality where they grow, but in the higher groups of plants there are big differences. In mosses, liverworts and ferns the two phases are quite different, and the haploid ones are even given different names—such as prothallium and protonema. Some of these plants are very suitable for the study of inheritance. The common moss, *Funaria hygrometrica*, has green gametophytes containing nuclei with seven chromosomes and brown sporophytes with nuclei containing fourteen. The diploid sporophytes grow from a zygote formed by the fusion of an ovum and an antherozooid (sperm) which were produced by the haploid gametophyte ; the sporophyte forms spores which give rise to haploid gametophytes. The progeny from the gametes of any haploid plant form a pure line, as the diploid phase (sporophyte) contains two sets of chromosomes, both derived from the same set, and therefore similar.

Von Wettstein, who has studied the genetics of this moss, succeeded in breeding pure lines of different characters—for instance, a broad-leaved line and a narrow-leaved line, which both breed true. When a cross was made from these two lines, the resulting sporophyte produced spores which were alike in appearance but different in the plants to which they gave rise. Sporophytes of this species produce batches of four spores, which are called tetraspores, and by a special technique it was possible to isolate the four spores which were descendants from a single spore mother-cell, and to germinate them. The result of one such experiment was as follows: from the thirty-five tetrads where the procedure succeeded two broad-leaved and two narrow-leaved moss plants were obtained in each case. Recently doubts have been expressed about von Wettstein's results, but similar results have since been obtained with some liverworts and Ascomycetes (fungi), but as these are more complicated, von Wettstein's examples are retained.

The inheritance of the two characters, broad-leaved and narrow-leaved, may seem quite simple, and so it is, but nevertheless it needs some formulation. This serves a useful purpose, as more complicated modes of inheritance can be better understood when a formal scheme has been evolved from a simple case. Let us say that each cell, including the gametes, of the haploid broad-leaved mosses contains something called *B*, while each cell of the narrow ones contains something called *b*. If sporophytes are made from zygotes produced by the union of two gametes, three kinds of sporophytes can be formed from the two kinds of gametes: *BB*, *Bb*, *bb*. It may be clearer to show this relationship in a table:

HAPLOID PARENTS GAMETOPHYTES	DIPLOID PHASE SPOROPHYTE	HAPLOID PROGENY GAMETOPHYTES
$B \times B$	*BB*	*B* *B*
$B \times b$ or $b \times B$	*Bb*	*B* *b*
$b \times b$	*bb*	*b* *b*

In the second line $B \times b$ and $b \times B$ are noted separately, as it is usual to write the female parent first; therefore the first product describes the cross of an ovum derived from a broad-leaved moss with the sperm of a narrow-leaved moss, and the second product is the reciprocal cross.

The *BB* and *bb* diploid sporophytes, which each give offspring of one kind only, are called homozygotes or homozygous sporophytes. The *Bb* plants give offspring of two kinds—namely, broad- and narrow-leaved plants, as was described above; they are called heterozygotes. *B* and *b* are called genes. Originally this term, which was first used by the Danish botanist Johanssen, did not mean much more than can be derived from its use in the case of the broad- and narrow-leaved mosses; it meant an inborn factor which determines the properties of organisms and persists in a manifest or hidden way through the generations. Nowadays one may think of the gene as a cell organ situated in a chromosome and reproducing itself exactly at each cell division, except for occasional disasters, and which does not reproduce otherwise.

If either one or the other of a pair of properties, like the possession of broad or narrow leaves, is alternately present in plants of a species, one assumes that there are two different genes which occupy corresponding places in corresponding chromosomes of the differing plants. Such pairs of genes as *B* and *b* are called allelomorphs or alleles, and in one chromosome of a set, and thus in every cell everywhere in a haploid plant, only one of them can be present; but in a diploid plant or in animals where two sets of chromosomes are commonly found, both alleles may occur in the same cell. This has been shown in our example, where, however, it referred to the diploid phase of a haploid–diploid plant. It is possible in some cases to find more than two alleles—three or even a whole series may occur, and they usually show in a graded property of their carrier. A well-known example of such a gradation is found in the eye-colour of some insects—for instance, in *Drosophila melanogaster*, where the eye can show many intermediate shades and colours, from the normal shining red at one end of the scale to complete white at the other.

CHAPTER VII

Mendelism in Diploids

IT has just been mentioned that in a diploid plant or animal —which means in the great majority of flowering plants and multicellular animals—most of the cells contain two sets of chromosomes. If two homologous genes—that is, alleles—can be found in such species, then individuals occur which have both those genes present together in every cell in the corresponding chromosomes of the two sets, and such individuals are called heterozygotes. It is very interesting to see what properties a heterozygous organism shows: is it controlled by one of the genes only, or is it influenced by both of them, and if so, is the influence of both genes of equal intensity, or does one predominate? In nature all these possibilities are fulfilled.

In the snapdragon, *Antirrhinum majus*, a mutant form has been described, under the name *graminifolia*, or grass-leaved, whose chief difference is that its leaves are narrower than those of the normal plant; in addition, there is a difference in the shape of the flowers, but that need not be taken into account here. The gene determining the ordinary wide-leaved form may be called *Gram*, and its allele determining the narrow-leaved form is then *gram*. If pollen is taken from a plant that produces broad leaves and breeds true in respect of leaf-shape, and is put on to the pistil of a plant from a true breeding stock with narrow leaves, the following results are obtained in the next two generations: in the first filial generation (F_1) only plants with broad leaves appear; in the second filial generation (F_2), produced by self-pollination of the F_1 plants, about three-quarters of the plants are broad-leaved and one-quarter are narrow. The gametes—that is, the pollen grains and ova—produced by the first plant, of which only the pollen was used, all carried one gene producing broad leaves, and the gametes of the other plant, of which only the ova were used, all carried one gene producing narrow leaves. Consequently plants of the first filial genera-

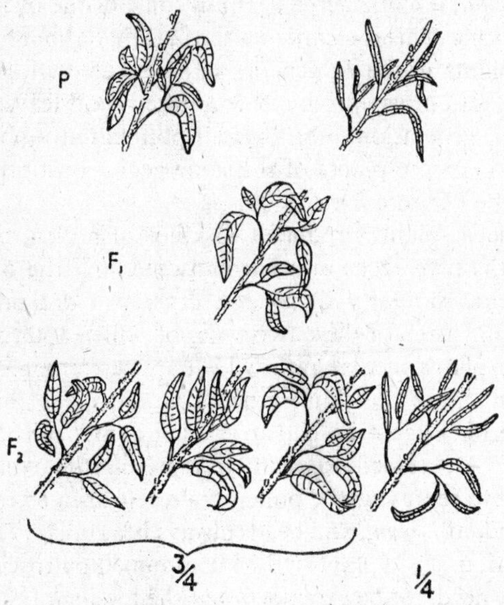

FIG. 8.—F_1 and F_2 generations from a cross between a wild type (broad-leaved) Antirrhinum and its mutant *graminifolia* (narrow-leaved).

tion all contain *Gram* in one chromosome and *gram* in the equivalent chromosome from the other parent.

Such an Antirrhinum carrying two chromosomes in its cells, one with the gene *Gram* and the other with the gene *gram*, is itself broad-leaved, and is described as being of the same *phenotype*, or appearance, as the father. Since *Gram* is the gene whose influence is exhibited in the whole plant when it is jointly present with *gram*, it is said to be dominant, while *gram*, which does not show in the presence of *Gram*, is said to be recessive. But although all the plants of the F_1 generation look like one of the parents, they have a different gene content—that is, they are of a different *genotype*—and although *gram* does not show in the presence of its dominant allele *Gram*, it can emerge again in some of the offspring of these plants. This is clear from the fact that about a quarter of the plants in the F_2 generation have narrow leaves, and this generation was produced from the broad-leaved plants of the F_1 generation either by self-pollination or by cross-fertilization from plants of the same genic constitution and phenotype (Figure 8).

All the F_1 plants produce two kinds of pollen, one containing the *Gram* gene in a chromosome, and the other the *gram* gene. Similarly *Gram* and *gram* ova are produced. The combination of these two types of pollen and two types of ova explains the 3:1 ratio which appears among the offspring in the second filial generation. To make this clear, recourse may again be had to tossing coins; but this time two coins are needed—a penny to represent the ovum and a sixpence to represent the pollen grain. Heads may represent *Gram* and tails *gram*, and heads always beat tails. The genic constitution of the plant will be determined by tossing both coins. It need not be explained that the tossing of the penny (ovum) and of the sixpence (pollen) are quite independent events; therefore, if we assume that heads and tails have equal chances, we shall get equal numbers of combinations of:

penny head and sixpence head
" " " " tail
" tail " " head
" " " " tail

Out of these four possible combinations the first represents the homozygote carrying broad leaves; the second and third, although they are manufactured in different ways, are both heterozygotes and of similar genetic constitution, and thus symbolize plants of similar appearance, and, since heads are present in both, they must represent plants with broad leaves. The last combination is homozygous for the recessive which is symbolized by tails, and therefore it represents plants with narrow leaves. In an actual experiment where coins were tossed the four combinations turned up in the following proportions:

penny	head	×	sixpence	head	259
,,	,,	×	,,	tail	239
,,	tail	×	,,	head	246
,,	,,	×	,,	tail	256
					1000

These figures show a very close approximation to the proportions $\frac{1}{4}$ to $\frac{1}{2}$ to $\frac{1}{4}$, and similar proportions are found in actual crossing experiments.

In the haploid mosses it has been shown that there are always four offspring (tetrads) from each fertilization, and when a cross is made, two of one kind and two of the other result; from the union of a male cell and an ovum in the flowering plants and in most animals, although there are four potential ova, only one matures, and the other three perish (Figure 18). Which of the four is preserved and which perish is not usually dependent on the genic constitution, although it can be in some species; hence the genic constitution, and consequent phenotype, of each offspring of a cross is subject to chance. For this reason a very large number of offspring is needed before information can be obtained about the frequencies of the possible combinations—much larger than is necessary in the case of haploid plants.

It has now been shown that snapdragons of different genic constitution can have the same appearance or phenotype, since both *Gram Gram* and *Gram gram* plants have broad leaves; such plants can only be distinguished from one another by breeding. If both types are crossed with a true breeding recessive plant of the genic constitution *gram gram* the results will be different in the two cases. This procedure is called back-crossing, because it involves crossing back to one of the ancestral stocks. Crossing the homozygous *Gram Gram* with *gram gram* will produce 100 per cent *Gram gram* plants, all having broad leaves, whereas crossing *Gram gram* with *gram gram* will produce about 50 per cent *Gram gram* with broad leaves and about 50 per cent *gram gram* plants with narrow leaves.

In some plants and animals the heterozygous form does not have the same phenotype as one of the homozygotes, and the types can be distinguished simply by inspection. In these cases there is a new type in the F_1 generation, which usually has an appearance intermediate between the two ancestral stocks. In the F_2 generation there are then three phenotypes which occur in the following proportions: approximately a quarter resembles one ancestral strain, a second quarter resembles the other ancestor and half are intermediate. The plants showing the ancestral characters will breed true if they are either self-fertilized or pollinated with pollen from plants of the same group, the intermediate plants will split in their progeny again, giving rise to a quarter homozygous for one allele, a quarter homozygous for the other allele and one-half intermediate. The intermediates will always split in the next generation.

Intermediate inheritance of characters that are determined by a single gene is far less common than the dominant type of inheritance. The most famous example of it is found in the Japanese flower *Mirabilis jalapa*, in which white and red flowering strains are known. The intermediate form produced in the first filial generation, when red and white are crossed, is pink, and this gives rise, when self-fertilized, to about a quarter white, one-half pink and a quarter red progeny. In the Chinese primrose, *Primula sinensis*, a cross between a 'Duchess' plant, whose flowers are white with a pink centre, and full red plants produces intermediate offspring, which if selfed produce offspring of the same intermediate type, as well as both parental forms.

Another example of intermediate inheritance occurs in Verbena. Here two alleles are found which when the plants are homozygous produce either deeply coloured or very pale flowers. In the heterozygous form these alleles produce flowers of an intermediate shade, and if the two homozygotes are crossed three sorts of offspring can be reared from this first cross. In an actual experiment the proportions in the F_2 generation were as follows:

GENIC CONSTITUTION	SHADE	NUMBER
DD	deeply coloured	76
Dd	pale	210
dd	very pale	98

These figures do not at a first glance show a very close approximation to the proportion 1:2:1, but statistical methods show that they do not deviate significantly from this proportion, for such numbers could occur in about every nineteenth experiment by chance (see page 27).

It may be argued that it is not very consistent to denote deep as *D* and very pale as *d*, as deep is not dominant over very pale, and therefore one should perhaps write *D* and *P* or *d* and *p* for the two alleles. Some justification for writing *Dd* and not *pP* may be found in the fact that the deeply coloured form, although it is not dominant in the experiment described, is by far the commoner of the two types, and can therefore be assumed to be the wild type.

In the budgerigar a mutant 'dark' is known to breeders which in single dose turns the light green breast of the normal bird into a dark green; in double dose it causes an olive colour.

Two examples from mouse-breeding may also be given. Albinotic mice—that is, mice with pink eyes and white coats—always breed true. There is another stock of mice which, though they are not white, are much lighter in colour than the ordinary house mouse, and which have dark ruby eyes. This stock is called extreme dilute, meaning that the usual fur colour seems to have been diluted. These pale mice can also be made to breed true. The offspring of a cross from the two stocks appear to be intermediate, with dark eyes but nearly white fur. If these intermediates are crossed back to individuals from the two parent stocks they give rise to offspring half of which are approximately like the parental stock chosen, while the other half are intermediate. If two individuals from the F_1 generation are crossed, three types of offspring appear: approximately a quarter resemble one of the original stocks, another quarter resemble the other original stock and one-half are intermediate. If we wrote this result in the form that we have used before we should do it as follows: extreme dilute would appear as $c^e c^e$, albino as cc and dark-eyed white as $c^e c$. It should be noted that the heterozygote is not really intermediate in the same sense that the pink Mirabilis flower is, but that one expression of the gene—the dark-red eye-colour—is taken from one parent, whereas the fur colour resembles the albino parent, though it is not exactly like it. Intermediate inheritance also occurs in man, but on the whole it is exceptional in most organisms, and dominant inheritance is the general rule.

Intermediate inheritance of one genetical character must

not be confused with polygenic inheritance, where many sets of alleles may determine such properties as the size or weight of an organism, and where offspring which have one very large or one very small parent will usually be found to be themselves somewhere in between the two extremes.

As we have already suggested, more than two alleles can occur in a diploid species, and then pairs which show all possible combinations occur in various individuals. This is the case with the human blood groups, which will be dealt with in more detail in a later chapter.

CHAPTER VIII

Polyhybrids and Linkage

In the last chapter crosses between plants or animals were discussed in which the two parents differed by one gene only. These are known as monohybrids. This one mutant gene was assumed to have its equivalent gene, or allelomorph, in the same place in the wild-type chromosome, and the mutant and wild-type genes are then said to occupy the same locus. Examples can now be considered of crosses from parents differing by several characters. These characters may be the consequence of one single mutational difference, and then it is said that the gene has several expressions, or that it is pleiotropic. In this case all the characters must be jointly inherited. Alternatively the characters may become dissociated more or less easily, and we assume, then, that each character is caused by a different gene. Such cases are called polyhybrids and will be discussed now. Before this is done some remarks are necessary concerning a particular relationship of genes.

Most mutants show independently in an individual, or influence each other only to a slight extent, so that it is always possible to spot them; but sometimes a mutant will not show in the presence of another or, alternatively, will show only if another is present. An example of one gene obscuring another is seen in the albino condition in many mammals; if it is present it may suppress the effects of other genes affecting fur colour. Examples of the second relationship are provided by the so-called modifiers, whose only known effect is to induce an alteration of the particular mutant effect.

The chromosomes are usually denoted by the Roman numerals I, II, III and so on, I usually being reserved for the larger of the two sex chromosomes, which is also called the X chromosome (see Chapter XI); the other numerals then refer to the autosomes. Let us consider the following experiment, in which two different autosomes are involved and a variety characterized by a single mutant gene is crossed with another variety differing from the wild type by a second mutant gene. Assuming that both the mutants are recessive the following genetic constitutions are found: one parent—in Figure 9 a male Drosophila fly—has two chromosomes II with the mutant *vg* (vestigial wing) in both, and two chromosomes III carrying the wild-type allele of *e* (ebony body colour), which is called *e*+, signifying normal lighter coloration; but the female has two chromosomes II with *vg*+ (normal wings), and two chromosomes III with the mutant gene *e*.

The F_1 generation which develops from the union will have one paternal chromosome II containing mutant *vg*, and a maternal chromosome II containing the wild-type allele *vg*+; the paternal chromosome III will contain the mutant *e* and the maternal chromosome III its wild-type allele *e*+. As *vg* and *e* are both recessives, this F_1 generation will have the appearance of the wild type, and will not show either of the mutant characters, but genetically it is different from a pure-bred wild stock, and this can be proved by breeding from it.

If a brother and sister of the F_1 generation are mated the mutant characters will appear in some of the offspring, either separately or united in the same individuals. If the constitution of the gametes produced by the members of the F_1 generation is considered, it is seen that there are four possible types for both eggs and sperms, since the chromosomes are distributed independently during meiosis (see Ch. IX). The following combinations may occur in both sexes :

Chromosome II carrying *vg* with chromosome III carrying *e*+
" " *vg* " " " *e*
" " *vg*+ " " " *e*+
" " *vg*+ " " " *e*

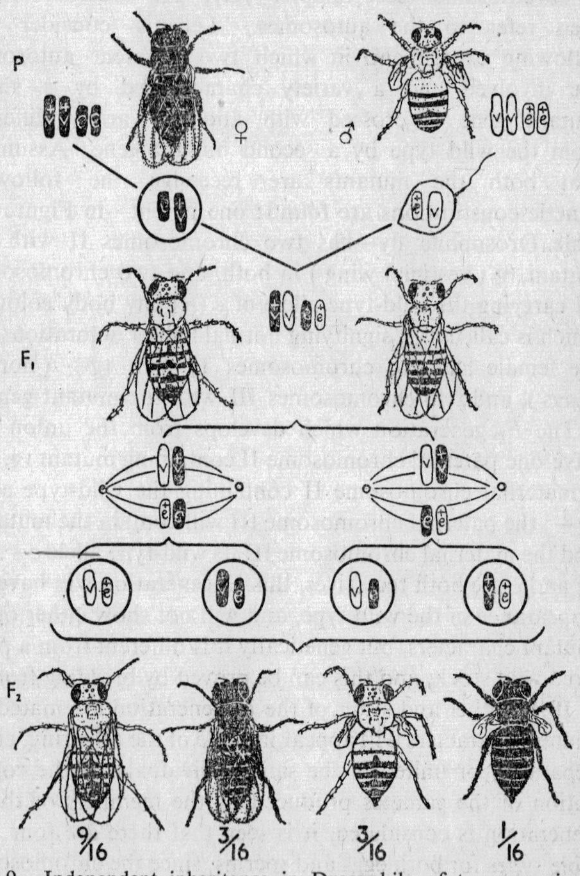

FIG. 9.—Independent inheritance in Drosophila of two recessives, ebony body colour and vestigial wings, introduced by different parents.

As all these possibilities have equal chances of occurring the result of their combination in the F_2 generation can be seen in the bottom row of Figure 9. Four phenotypes are possible. Three of these may be heterozygous—one in two ways; and as the genes under consideration are recessive any individual which is heterozygous for one of the genes will show the character of the wild type; therefore the 9 : 3 : 3 : 1 distribution of the individuals of the F_2 generation results. Approximately $\frac{9}{16}$ will have the appearance of the wild type, $\frac{3}{16}$ will show the mutant character *e*, another $\frac{3}{16}$ will show the mutant character *vg*, and $\frac{1}{16}$ will show both *e* and *vg*, which is a new combination. Only the last group will breed true. The first group will be complex, all its members being of the same phenotype but of different genotypes; therefore they will behave differently when they are bred from. Figure 9 is an illustration of the behaviour described, except that the F_2 males have been omitted.

If the two mutant genes are localized and transmitted in the same or in homologous autosomes the expectation would be that they would not be inherited independently, as in the example just given, but either jointly (coupling), or mutually excluding each other (repulsion). Both types of dependence in distribution are called *linkage*. Let us consider an example which at first sight is only a little different from the previous one—namely, the crossing of two stocks each of which is homozygous for one recessive gene. If, for instance, we take a strain of shaker mice and cross it with a strain of albino mice, we get an F_1 generation with normal body-colour and normal behaviour. Again in the F_2 generation four different types appear but in different ratios; instead of $\frac{9}{16}$ being of the wild type, $\frac{3}{16}$ shakers, $\frac{3}{16}$ albinos and $\frac{1}{16}$ shaker albinos, there are much fewer than $\frac{1}{16}$ of the last, the double recessive class, and more of the single recessives. Thus there is some 'repulsion' between the genes, but not a complete one. This is due to the breaking and exchange of segments in paired chromosomes—a process called crossing-over, which will be described later (page 77). If the two mutant genes introduced from different parents are localized more distantly on homologous chromosomes than happened in our cross, repulsion will be decreased or absent.

If, on the other hand, both mutant genes are introduced by one parent, the F_2 generation obtained by mating this homozygous albinotic shaker stock with a wild-type mouse would give, not $\frac{9}{16}$ wild-type mice, $\frac{3}{16}$ shakers, $\frac{3}{16}$ albinos and $\frac{1}{16}$ albino shakers, but too many of the double recessives and too few of the single recessives. The two characters appear in coupling. Experiments of this second type yield statistically more valuable results, as the rare classes tend to be increased rather than decreased by the crossing over. The percentage by which the recombination figures are altered from the 9 : 3 : 3 : 1 ratio gives a measure of the distances between the two loci on the chromosome. If crossing over approaches 50 per cent—the theoretical limit—it cannot be decided directly whether two loci are localized in the same chromosome or not; this can be done only if more than two mutants are combined. In practice it will be found that there are all degrees of distribution of characters in a progeny, ranging from free recombination—that is, agreement with the 9 : 3 : 3 : 1 ratio, irrespective of whether the genes were introduced into the cross jointly or separately—to complete coupling or repulsion.

There is one important result from the study of linkage: in all the cases which have been most thoroughly investigated the number of the groups of linked characters corresponds to the haploid number of chromosomes, except in certain special cases where chromosomes of a particular appearance seem to carry no genes at all. The function of these so-called inert chromosomes, which occur in some plants and insects, is still rather obscure. The equality of the chromosome numbers with the numbers of linkage groups not only supports the chromosome theory of inheritance to a high degree, but it is also a proof of the constancy and individuality of the chromosomes. Further proofs of chromosome individuality are supplied by direct observation.

In *Drosophila melanogaster* and some of its relations crossing over between the autosomes occurs during the formation of eggs only, and not during spermatogenesis—that is, in the female and not in the male—but crossing over takes place during spermatogenesis between the homologous parts of the X and Y chromosomes. We do not yet understand the significance of all this, but it makes it easier to distinguish between independent and linked inheritance. If two characters keep together in the male but get separated in the female, then they must be linked in one chromosome; if they separate in both sexes they are localized in different chromosomes.

Figure 10 illustrates a crossing experiment in Drosophila, in which the method of back-crossing is used. On the left side a male of an F_1 generation from a cross between a dihybrid and a wild type is mated back to a female from the dihybrid stock, and the offspring in the second generation show the original types only. However, the reciprocal cross between the doubly heterozygous female and the dihybrid male, which is shown on the right, produces not only the wild type and the dihybrid forms, but also monohybrid forms, thus giving a new character combination not so far observed in the ancestry. The figures of 8·5 per cent and 17 per cent, indicating the proportion of new combinations, are called the recombination figures. Their significance in the localization of genes in chromosomes or, as one sometimes says, in the drawing of chromosome maps, will be explained later.

To decide whether three mutant characters are localized in one, two or three different chromosomes rather more elaborate methods are necessary, but they can easily be derived from the example given. Furthermore, mutant genes localized in the X chromosome show a different type of inheritance, which is described on page 85.

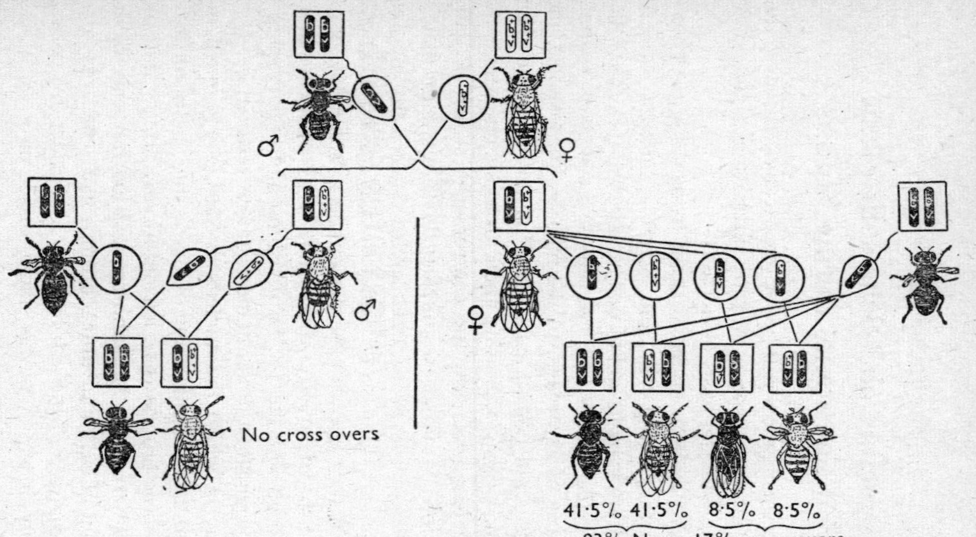

FIG. 10.—Cross of a double recessive (black vestigial) male and a wild type female in Drosophila, and back cross of both male and female offspring to the double recessive type. Crossing over takes place only in the female.

CHAPTER IX

Structure and Behaviour of the Chromosomes during Mitosis

THE next two chapters will be the most technical ones in this book, but in many respects the most interesting, as they show what is the material basis of heredity.

It has already been stated that all living cells are descendants of other living cells, and that the simplest form of multiplication is by fission of one mother cell into two equal daughter cells. This is true not only of the cell as a whole but of many of its organs, of the nucleus, for instance, and also of its main constituents, the chromosomes and their regions and organs, including the chromomeres, where the genes are localized, and the centromeres, which actually direct fission. In most cases nuclear division is immediately followed by cell division, and therefore most cells are uninuclear, but sometimes multi-nuclear cells can be observed, like those which occur in the plasmodia of some Myxomycetes or in the malaria parasite. Cellular division can, however, catch up with the nuclear divisions, and in some stages of these organisms the uni-nuclear state is restored.

The way in which the nucleus divides is very much the same in all higher animals and plants, and in most Protozoa, and the whole process is called mitotic division or mitosis; it is characterized by an elaborate division not only of the nucleus but of each individual chromosome, which may precede the division of the cell body by a considerable period. Very rarely does the nucleus simply divide into two lumps, and where this is the case—as it may be in inflamed tissue or in the dying skin—the resulting cells are not capable of proper reproduction. In Infusoria, where the macro-nucleus normally divides in this artless way, the micro-nucleus divides mitotically. The whole process of mitosis is an elaborate way of ensuring that the genes which are localized in the chromo-

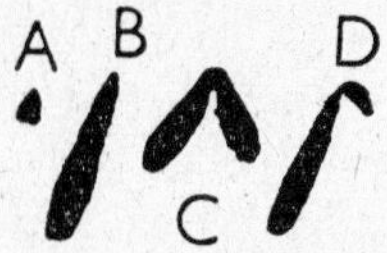

FIG. 11.—Forms of chromosomes at mitosis. A = a short chromosome from the plant *Yucca filamentosa*, B = rod-shaped chromosome from a grasshopper *Stenobothrus lineatus*, C = V-shaped two armed chromosome from a prunus, D = J-shaped chromosome from a tulip.

somes shall be exactly distributed among the daughter nuclei. The chromosomes are not equally easy to see at all phases of this nuclear cycle or in all sorts of cells, but usually if they are suitably stained they become visible during mitosis. Typically they are somewhat elongated bodies

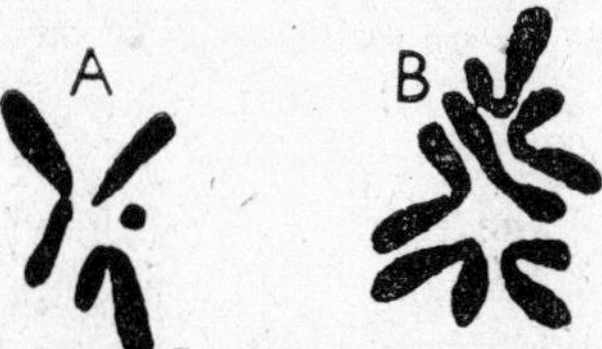

FIG. 12.—A. Chromosome set of the fruit-fly, *Drosophila melanogaster*, composed of the rod-shaped sex chromosome (X), two V-shaped chromosomes (II and III) and the short fourth chromosome. B. Chromosome set of the plant *Tradescantia bractata*, composed of six V-shaped chromosomes. (After Darlington, 1937.)

which stain with the so-called basic dyes, such as hæmatoxylin or carmine, but they can have very different shapes. Figure 11 shows some of these. They may be short bodies (*A*), or rods (*B*), or V- or J-shaped (*C, D*). Figure 12 shows how different types of chromosomes may sometimes occur in the same nucleus, as in Drosophila (*A*), instead of all of them being more or less alike, as in the plant Tradescantia (*B*); when they are of different types it is easier to distinguish between the individual chromosomes.

Although the chromosomes do not appear in the same shape during the whole cycle of cell division, or in different cells of the same organism, there is no doubt that each one always retains its individuality, principally the content and order of its genes, even when it becomes temporarily invisible between two nuclear divisions during the so-called resting stage of the nucleus. The bulk, length and affinity

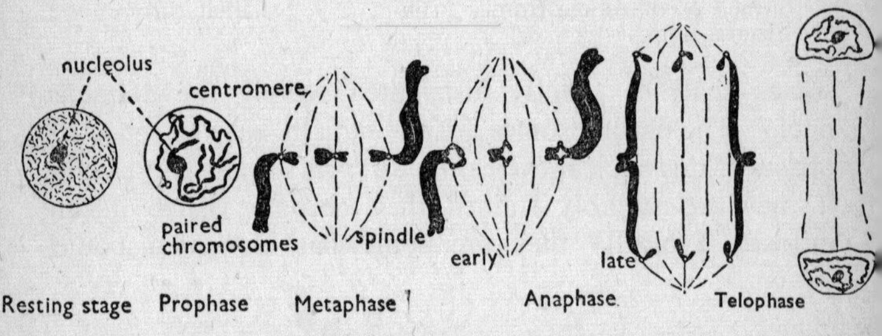

FIG. 13.—Mitotic cycle of a cell nucleus containing three chromosomes.

with dyestuffs of the chromosomes show regular changes during the cycles through which they pass. Each contains either in the middle or nearer to one end a centromere, and this organ will be seen to play an important part in the attraction and separation of the chromosomes. In one chromosome of each cell there is another organ, the nucleolus, which has the shape of a bladder and contains mostly nucleic acid.

The mitotic cycle of a cell nucleus is shown in Figure 13. The first sign of mitosis is that the chromosomes, which are thin, long and loosely packed in the resting stage, become more easily separable under the microscope as they gradually contract and thicken owing to coiling and the apposition of material; this stage constitutes the prophase. In the following stage—the metaphase—the nucleolus and nuclear membrane disappear, and the chromosomes, which now lie in the cytoplasm, become attached by the centromeres to a structure called the spindle. The nature of the spindle is not clearly known, but it is certainly of importance for division. The chromosomes lie near the equatorial plane—that is, the plane separating the two future cells—in various ways which are typical for different species. In Salamandra, for instance, the centromeres lie at the edge of the spindle and the bodies of the chromosomes lie outside in the cytoplasm. Frequently the centromeres lie evenly in the equatorial plane of the spindle and the chromosomes lie inside the spindle, flat on the plate when they are small and turned up on either side when they are long. In favourable material it can be seen that the chromosome threads have divided and are double from an early stage—certainly in the prophase, if not earlier—and each half is called a chromatid.

In the anaphase, which follows, the chromosomes begin to separate: first the two centromeres, and later on the chromatids, are pulled apart, the ends which are not attached to the spindle being the last parts to come away. When the separation is complete the two groups of corresponding daughter chromosomes pass towards opposite poles of the spindle, and during the following telophase they uncoil and again become thin and long. They finally form an entangled mass and enter a new resting stage while new nucleoli and nuclear membranes develop; at the same time division of the cell body proceeds. The time taken by one nuclear division usually varies between some minutes and several hours, but the resting stage can last very much longer.

The chromosomes, as already mentioned, do not preserve their length and shape throughout mitosis, nor do they always stain in the same way. The contractions of the chromosomes during the telophase and prophase depend on spiralization: when the chromosomes become longer they are uncoiling, and during the metaphase the coils contract again. Thus each chromosome may be visualized as a sort of wool thread or wire spiral where the coiling leads to the appearance of a smooth, rod-shaped body. When such a spiral uncoils the apparently straight shape disappears and the coiling becomes visible until almost complete extension is reached. If it is assumed that the genes are localized along the thread, the distances between them become greater when the chromosomes are uncoiled.

Of course chromosomes are not really wool or wire, but rather long chains of protein material, and they are not stretched by pulling at the ends, but most likely by the intake of water from the cytoplasm—the less water the chromosome contains the shorter it is, and its water content also controls its affinity for histological dyes.

CHAPTER X

Meiosis and Crossing Over

SOME knowledge of the mechanism of meiosis is essential for an understanding of genetics, because at this stage much of the 'shuffling' and 'dealing' of the genes occurs, by which some of the material of the grandparents of an organism is eliminated and the rest rearranged before it enters the gamete. It has already been said that even as early as 1887 Weismann concluded that in the life-cycle of sexual organisms there must be a nuclear division, in the course of which what we now call the genes and chromosomes are reduced in amount in such a way that each daughter nucleus receives only half the number. If this were not so more and more chromosomes would accumulate, owing to fertilization, until the cells would be completely filled with them. Such a recurrent pathological process has been observed in a fern, and the offspring are dwarfed and hardly viable.

In fact, there are always two successive nuclear divisions —the meiotic divisions, during which the halving of the chromosome number occurs. In the higher animals meiosis happens shortly before the germ cells are formed, and in higher plants before the production of pollen and oögonia. During the first meiotic division the centromeres do not divide, while the chromosomes do—a process which might be described by stating that the internal mechanism by which each chromosome produces two chromatids gets out of step with the external mechanism of spindle formation. A simple example of meiosis as it happens in a pollen mother-cell of Fritillaria may be given in a schematic form. Figure 14 shows only what happens to one pair of chromosomes during this process, but the same thing applies to all of them. The cycles of the nuclear membrane and of the nucleolus—a body included in the nucleus—are indicated, but all other structures, as well as divisions of the cytoplasm, have been omitted, as they vary a great deal and are not essential for an understanding of meiosis. A certain familiarity with a dozen or so of the technical terms used in describing meiosis is necessary for the understanding of many genetical papers, and therefore these terms have not been omitted, but it is more important to understand what is happening to the chromosome than to remember the names of the various phases.

Leptotene: the diploid number of chromosomes, paternal and maternal, appears in the nucleus; they look like chains of unequal beads strung at unequal distances. *Zygotene:* the chromosomes which were previously distributed throughout the nucleus come together in pairs, as if they were attracted by each other, and the individual chromomeres (genes) come thus to lie very close to each other, and after a while the whole complement are present as double threads in the haploid number. *Pachytene:* the paired threads (bivalents) coil around one another and show a higher degree of contraction. It is important to realize that bivalents are different in origin from splitting chromatids. *Early diplotene:* the chromosomes begin to separate, and now each is seen to be double, consisting of two chromatids which remain closely associated. The separation of the chromosomes is not always complete, however—they stick at one or several points where one paternal and one maternal chromatid exchange partners. This is achieved by breakage at corresponding places of the two chromatids, possibly owing to the stress produced by the coiling, and by subsequent rejoining. Thus as a consequence of one 'crossing over' of the four chromatids one remains completely paternal, one maternal and two are mixed. This is the reason why crossing over never occurs

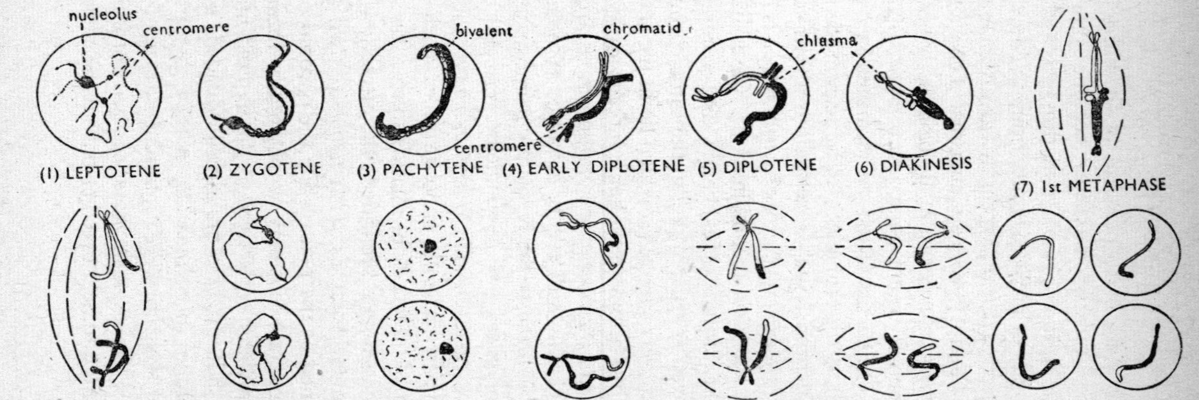

FIG. 14.—Meiotic divisions of one chromosome, either an autosome, or a sex chromosome in the homogametic sex.

more frequently than in 50 per cent of the chromosomes. *Later diplotene:* the chromosomes become shorter and thicker through further coiling, and thus successive loops between the points of breakage and rejoining come to lie at right angles. From a certain aspect this arrangement has the form of a cross, and it is called a chiasma. The exchange of chromatid segments can occasionally be directly observed in process of happening, and if some structural peculiarities are attached to two segments which get separated in a chromosome, the result of the exchange can be seen in the chromosomes of the offspring. Such observations afford very good confirmation of the genetical crossing over which is based on inference from the gene recombinations. Cases have been described where structural exchange and recombination have been proved to go parallel in the same chromosome. This finding explains why genes which lie in the same chromosome, and thus belong to the same linkage group, are not absolutely linked. *Diakinesis:* the chromosomes are at their shortest, but they are still evenly dispersed throughout the nucleus. *First metaphase:* the bivalent chromosomes are arranged at the equatorial plane in such a way that each has one centromere on each side. *First anaphase:* the centromeres of each pair move to opposite poles, each drawing after it the pair of attached chromatids so that the segments distal to the chiasma are separated; the attraction between the paired chromatids lapses. *First telophase:* two daughter nuclei are formed at the poles while the chromosomes uncoil; the two separate cells may or may not be formed. The two daughter nuclei have arrived at the haploid number of chromosomes, but, as these are already divided, they have the diploid number of chromatids, as they have in the mitotic telophase; a resting stage (interphase) may or may not be conspicuous. *Second metaphase:* the two chromatids are widely separated, and held together only at the centromeres.

Second anaphase: the chromosomes are distributed and behave as in the first anaphase. *Second telophase:* four daughter nuclei are formed, each receiving the haploid number of chromatids.

The reduction of the chromosome number during meiosis is thus effected by the failure of the centromere to divide during the first division. During the second division it is the centromere that divides, and the chromatids merely move apart. Thus, if there is no chiasma formation (no crossing over), both the chromatids descended from one chromosome, either paternal or maternal, get into the same nucleus after the first division and are separated only in the second division. If one chiasma is formed, two chromatids are not affected by it, but in the two other exchanges are effected in the following way: the segments nearer to the centromere are still the original ones, but the distal segments have been exchanged. It ought to be mentioned, in anticipation of the chapter on sex determination, that in the sex containing two X chromosomes—that is, the homogametic sex—the X chromosomes pair or form bivalents during meiosis much as the autosomes do. This applies to the females of mammals and of most insects, with the exception of the Lepidoptera and Trichoptera—in these two orders and in the birds the male is the homogametic sex. In the heterogametic sex either the sex chromosomes do not pair, as they are present only singly, or only the regions pair which are identical in the X and the Y chromosomes and not the regions which are different. At present not much is known about the process causing the attraction or repulsion of chromosomes, chromatids and chromomeres in the various phases of mitosis and meiosis; it is even uncertain whether the chromosomes are dragged along by the centromere or carried away by currents in the liquid surrounding them, or whether they actively push their way. However, it seems certain that want of oxygen or the presence of various poisons can inhibit nuclear division or arrest it at various stages.

The chromosomes of most cells are rather small, and even if they can be well stained during mitosis and meiosis the resolving power of the microscope is rarely sufficient to show

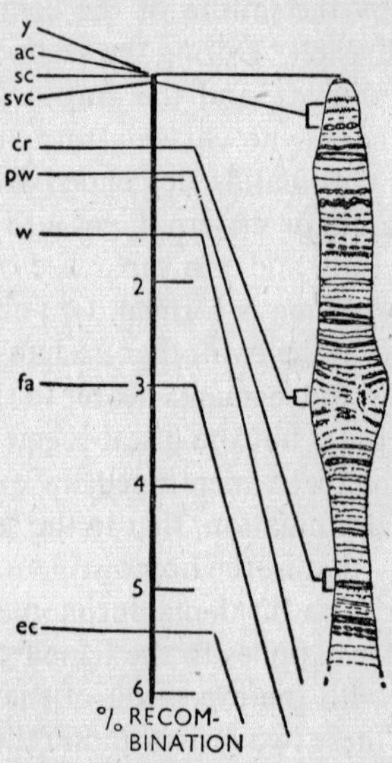

FIG. 15.—The bands in part of the sex chromosome in a salivary gland of *Drosophila melanogaster* and the linear arrangement and distance of mutant loci referred from recombination percentages. The mutant loci on the left are: yellow = a body colour, achæte = lack of certain hair and bristles, scute = loss of other bristles, silver = a body colour, white = an eye colour, facet = irregular eye facets, echinous = large facets in eyes.

many details in their structure. This difficulty may some day be overcome by the use of the electron microscope, but meanwhile a lucky accident has contributed very much to the progress of genetics and cytology. Long after the work on Drosophila had been started, because of the many advantages of this fly as an object of genetical study, it was detected that the salivary glands of the third instar of its larva showed gigantic chromosomes. These had previously been described without their nature having been realized. These giant chromosomes, which are also found in other Dipterous

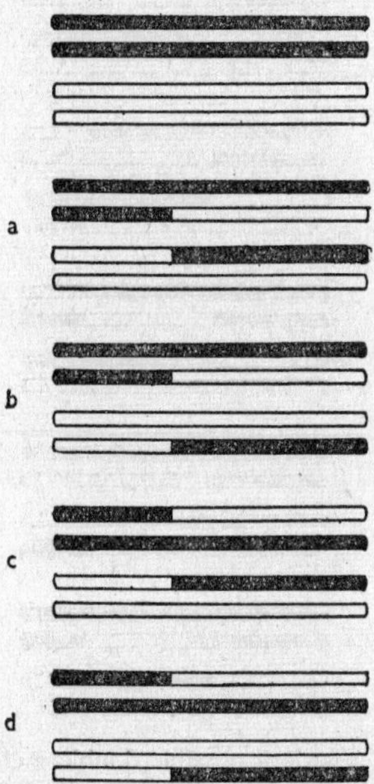

FIG. 16.—The four possible single crossovers between non-sister chromatids always producing two crossover and two non-crossover chromatids. (Redrawn from Sturtevant and Beadle, 1940.)

larvæ and in some organs other than the salivary glands, are composed of two paired groups of sixty-four or 128 individual chromatids each, all uncoiled and lying chromomere to chromomere; of course the X chromosome in the male is not paired. Inversions where the order of the chromatids does not correspond in the two groups cause loops which can easily be seen under the microscope. Figure 15 shows a part of the giant X chromosome with the corresponding part of a recombination map.

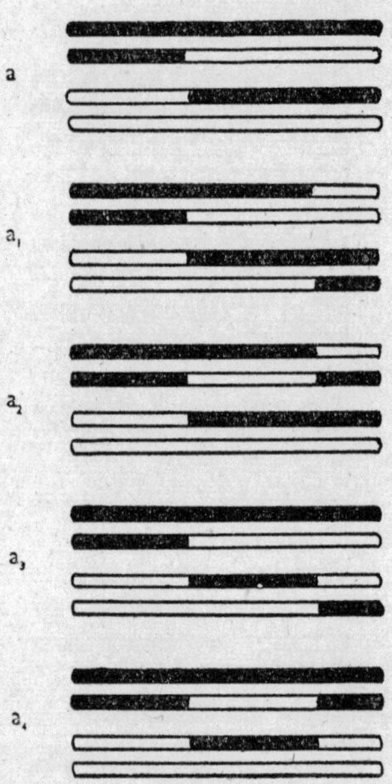

FIG. 17.—Four of the sixteen possible double exchanges in a tetrad. In the top tetrad, from which the four crossovers on the right are deduced, the crossover on the left has been considered as fixed in the position of Figure 15, *a*. Equal numbers of non-crossovers, single crossovers on the left, single crossovers on the right, and double crossover chromatids result. (Redrawn from Sturtevant and Beadle, 1940.)

For a consideration of genetical crossing over, only chiasmata between non-sister chromatids—that is, between halves of paternal and maternal chromosomes—need be considered, and there is evidence that actually crossing over does not occur between sister chromatids. If, then, one single crossover occurs in a bivalent which is composed of four chromatids it will always result in two cross-over and two non-cross-over chromatids, independently of which chromatids are taking part in it (Figure 16). If, however, two separate chiasmata occur in a bivalent at different loci, it makes a difference whether the chromatids involved in the first exchange are identical with those participating in the second chiasma or not. Figure 17 shows that in principle four double exchanges may result, giving rise to four classes of chromatids: non-cross-overs, single cross-overs at both loci and double cross-overs. Even more varied is the production of multiple cross-overs, of which up to twelve have been observed in a single bivalent.

CHAPTER XI

The Inheritance of Sex: Sex-Linked and Sex-Limited Characters

IT has already been mentioned that male and female organs can be found together in one individual. This is the case in the majority of flowering plants, and, among animals, in most snails and earthworms and in some others. In plants the condition is called monoecious, while in animals it is known as hermaphrodite. Normally in such species all individuals are alike, and therefore the question of a method of determining the sex or of regulating the proportions of the sexes does not occur. The eggs and the spermatozoa differ in their appearance—for instance, the eggs, which are conspicuously larger, contain more material, but they do not as a rule differ in their genetical constitution because usually both carry the same numbers of chromosomes and of genes. Whether any part of a plant or animal of this type develops into a male or a female reproductive organ is determined by its position or the time of its development, or by some other physiological factor such as temperature. Physiological sex determination can also be found among bisexual animals such as the worm Bonellia, where a larva develops into a female when it is growing by itself and into a small semi-parasitic male when it grows embedded in a female. In the majority of bisexual organisms, however, the two different types of individuals found—that is, males and females—are determined genetically, and it is rarely that they can change from one into the other.

If the difference between maleness and femaleness is assumed to be genetical, the simplest imaginable arragement would be if sex were determined by a single pair of alleles—a situation nearly realized in the tropical fish Lebistes and in some newts, where the presence of one allele makes the individual develop into a male and of the other into a female. A similar situation is also found in some mosquitoes.

Another method of genetical sex determination was first detected in the bee, and was subsequently found in many species, notably among the Hymenoptera and the Rotifers. Here an unfertilized egg produces males, which consequently contain cells with the haploid chromosome number only. It is clear that meiosis in such a haploid male must be of quite an unusual type; in the drone, for example, the first meiotic division is almost completely suppressed, whereas meiosis in the queen bee involves the usual reduction from the diploid number of chromosomes. The existence of a haploid individual is in itself very curious, for all the genes in such a male's cells are present once only, while in the female's cells the double number are active. Obviously such exceptional behaviour needs regulative mechanisms that make both the haploid and the diploid individuals viable.

There are other rare and very interesting mechanisms for genetical sex determination, but we shall deal here only with the most common form; this is the production of two kinds of gametes by one sex, which is then called the heterogametic sex. For instance, flies and mammals, among them man, produce one kind of egg but two kinds of spermatozoa (Figure 18), whereas birds produce one kind of spermatozoon and two kinds of eggs. Most often the homogametic sex is characterized by the possession of two homologous chromosomes—the X chromosomes—giving gametes of uniform constitution all containing one X, while the heterogametic sex has two different sex chromosomes—X and Y—and produces gametes of two different types in approxim-

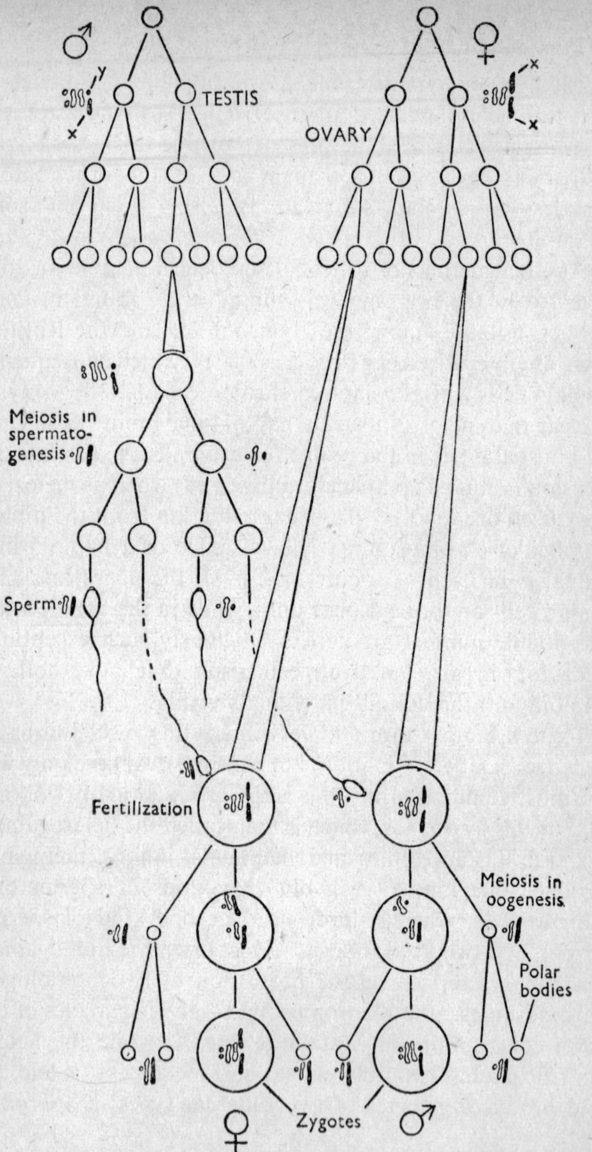

FIG. 18.—Formation of the ova and sperms and fertilization in a mammal. (Redrawn from Claus, Grobben and Kühn.)

ately equal numbers, half with X and half with Y. When a gamete containing X combines with one containing Y the zygote will be heterogametic, but where X combines with X a homogametic zygote will result. In this way generations can be perpetuated which will always show a sex ratio of approximately 1 : 1, and this is roughly the case in the overwhelming majority of bisexual organisms.

The morphological difference between the X and the Y chromosomes can be very slight and difficult to detect, as it is in *Drosophila virilis*, or the two chromosomes may differ to a greater extent, so that although part of their length is homologous another part is not; this happens in *Drosophila melanogaster*. In actual gene content, however, there need not be a great difference between the types. Clearly, pairing and crossing over can take place between the homologous parts but not between the segments that are present once only. The X chromosome, which is found paired in the homogametic sex, is usually larger, and probably contains more genes than the Y chromosome, for more mutants can be localized in it; the Y chromosomes of some species are regarded as being genetically rather inert, which means that they do not contain many genes. The extreme reduction of the Y chromosome, its complete absence, can be found normally in some species of grasshoppers and bugs, and exceptionally in *Drosophila melanogaster* and five other Drosophila species, in which the loss of the Y chromosome does not prevent the development of the male, but only causes it to be sterile.

The mechanism of sex determination can be demonstrated by means of sex-linked mutants. Such mutations can either be dominant, thus showing in the individual whether the gene in question is present singly in the heterogametic sex or in combination with the allele in the homogametic one, or they can be recessive, in which case their effect is visible in the heterogametic sex when present singly, but in the homogametic sex only when present doubly. A third type which is

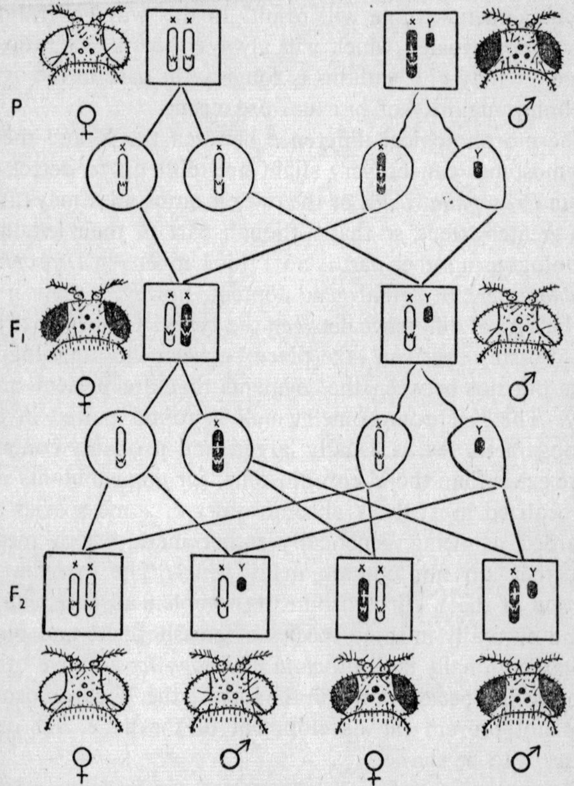

FIG. 19.—Cross between a sex-linked recessive (white eye) and a wild type in two generations of Drosophila.

fairly common shows quantitatively different effects, depending upon the presence of one or two mutant genes in an individual. These cases can be described as semi-dominant.

Figure 19 shows the criss-cross inheritance of the recessive mutant character white in Drosophila; it causes a total loss of pigment formation, so that the flies have white instead of red eyes. Another expression of the same gene is not only sex linked, but also sex limited, which means that it can in the nature of things show only in one sex—in this case in the male, as white in a Drosophila male causes the testis sheath, which normally is yellow, to become colourless. Obviously, as the female has no testis, this particular character cannot show. There are other sex-limited characters which need not be sex-linked. An example of a sex-linked recessive in man, with perhaps a slight suggestion of semi-dominance, is hæmophilia. (See Chapter XXI).

Sex-limited characters of economic importance introduce certain complications into practical husbandry. The yield of milk and its butter content, which can show only in a cow, can be much more easily influenced by selecting bulls than by selecting cows. This becomes obvious if one considers that a cow produces only a few female offspring, whereas a bull may service many hundreds of cows, and by means of artificial insemination may become the father of many thousands. The quality of a bull can only be inferred from testing his daughters and grand-daughters, and he should therefore be used as a sire on a large scale only after a progeny test has been carried out—that is, when he is about nine years old. Such practice presupposes great scientific insight and good organization among dairy-farmers. However, it has been tried in Denmark, where a large proportion of the dairy-cows owe their high butter production to two bulls.

A sex-determining mechanism working only with X chromosomes is logically very near akin to the haploid–diploid sex determination described in the bee; the difference is that in such a case there is only one sex chromosome, while in the bee all the chromosomes together act as sex chromosomes. Most commonly in cases where there is an X and a Y the presence of the part of the X which is not analogous to the Y decides the sex. Sex is then controlled by a balance between the sex chromosomes, or rather between the parts of them that are different, and the rest of the genes which are localized in the autosomes and in the part common to the X and Y. This is particularly clear in the Drosophila males having a Y chromosome.

In many species the development of all individuals starts on an apparently uniform course, and whether this continues in the direction of maleness or femaleness becomes apparent at a rather late stage, although a decision was made when the zygote was formed at fertilization. But this decision is not a final one, as the action of the genes can still be modified —for instance, one X chromosome in a female can be lost at a cell division, and the tissue developing from the cell containing only one X will then be male, and various types of gynandromorphs can thus develop. The organs may develop to a large extent independently, as they do in a fly, or they may influence each other greatly, as they do in the Vertebrates. Sexually abnormal types, such as intersexes and hermaphrodites, can also develop without the loss of a chromosome. This may happen owing to disturbances occurring in the agents by which the different organs influence each other—for instance, the hormones.

To understand this clearly a distinction must be drawn between species characters and sex characters. In this context a species character means a quality which would develop even in a castrated individual. Such a character is usually developed in one sex and modified in the other. In poultry, for instance, the male plumage shows mostly the species character, and in the female it is modified to its female appearance by hormones which are produced in the ovary. Consequently a castrated hen shows plumage rather similar to a cock's, and a senile hen also will be cock-feathered, but a castrated cock does not change its plumage. The comb of the cock, on the other hand, is a male sex character, and it does not develop either in a hen or in a castrated cockerel; it may even degenerate in a castrated adult.

CHAPTER XII

Mutations

A SUDDEN and permanent change of a gene is called a mutation. It has been shown that when the chromosomes split into their two chromatids identical genes are left in each of the halves unless an accident occurs. We shall now consider such accidents. During the complicated movements and rearrangements of the chromosomes which happen at mitosis and meiosis it is always possible that pieces may break off, and these pieces can get lost or they can be attached again to the same chromosome either in the right or in a wrong place. If the broken ends join in the old position no trace of the accident will remain after healing, but where they join in a different way the new arrangement of the genes that results in the chromosome can become permanent. When there is complete loss of some length of a chromosome a viable individual may still develop, but not if the loss becomes homozygous.

Frequently a segment of a chromosome becomes dislocated. It is easy to imagine that a loop in a chromosome may break at the point where the threads cross and that the threads may then join together at the wrong ends. This is called inversion, and it brings about a change in the sequence of gene loci; thus a gene sequence *A B C D E* may become the sequence *A D C B E.* If two homologous chromosomes, differing by one inversion, pair together a loop is formed between the non-inverted parts owing to the attraction of the individual loci. The configuration of this state is indicated in Figure 20. In the small chromosomes of ordinary cells *inversions* would be difficult to detect, but in the paired giant chromosomes of the salivary glands in Drosophila inversion loops are plainly visible under the microscope. Figure 21 shows such an inversion loop. It can be seen that homologous bands are paired in the non-inverted segments as well

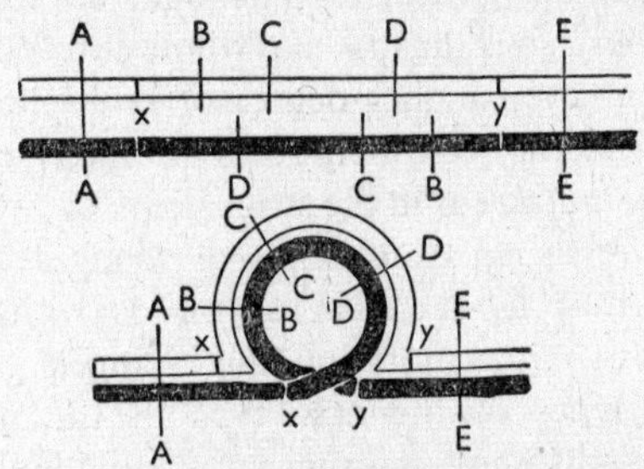

FIG. 20.—The loop formed in two pairing chromosomes differing by an inversion of the segment *x y*, including the loci B, C and D. The inversion must be due to a double break. The loop is brought about by the tendency of homologous loci to unite as closely as possible. (Redrawn from Sturtevant and Beadle, 1940.)

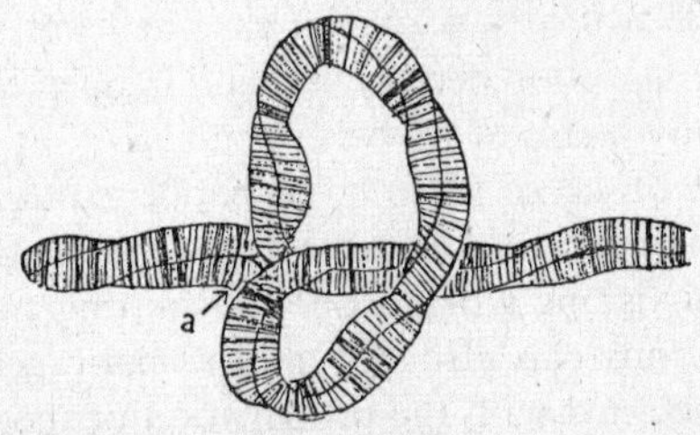

FIG. 21.—Appearance of an actual loop in the somatic pairing of giant chromosomes in the salivary glands of the larva of Drosophila. '*a*' marks the beginning and the end of the inversion causing the loop.

as in the inverted ones, except in a very small region (*a*) where the loop starts.

If two non-homologous chromosomes are broken at the same time, fragments may be exchanged, and the result is called *translocation*. The pieces of chromosomes involved in losses, inversions or translocations may vary in length from large sections to very small bits—so small that with the methods available they cannot be detected. All these spatial rearrangements of parts of chromosomes are called *chromosome mutations*; so is the loss of a whole chromosome, or the duplication or even higher degree of multiplication of the whole chromosome set which occurs in many plants (polyploidy); but mutations in the strict sense, or *gene mutations*, are usually regarded as qualitative changes of the genes themselves—that is, chemical or physical changes in the gene structure. After mutation the changed gene goes on to produce genes of the new type. If the new allele is dominant it will show in the first individual which has it in its nuclei; a sex-linked recessive will show in the first heterogametic individual carrying it, but autosomal recessives will show only after at least two generations of inbreeding.

It is not known in any special case at what stage of the nuclear cycle mutation occurs; it might happen in the resting stage or at any phase of mitosis or meiosis, but it will most frequently be observed when it has happened during the cell divisions in oögenesis and spermatogenesis, as the products from these divisions will go on transmitting the new property. Mutations can also occur in somatic cells—that is, cells not concerned with the propagation of the organism—and these are called somatic mutations. Here the mutating gene is not found in all the cells of the plant or animal, but only in some of them, and the result is the production of a mosaic. For instance, Drosophila flies may be found which have a white sector in an otherwise red eye, or which are differently coloured in different parts of the body.

The stability or otherwise of a gene can itself be controlled by one or several other genes, which then do not directly produce the effects observed, but only regulate the frequency of their occurrence.

Mutation of a gene may alter its effects to varying degrees. A gene, for instance, determining eye-colour in Drosophila may mutate in about a dozen different degrees, giving eyes of colours and shades ranging between the normal bright red through different kinds of pink and apricot to white. It can be shown that all these mutants are alleles—that is, that all the genes resulting in the different colours are set at the same place or locus in the same chromosome. Moreover, back mutations have been observed, which means that normally coloured eyes reappeared in the offspring of true breeding white-eyed flies. Obviously the normal gene has not been lost, but only changed, as it is improbable that it has originated anew from nothing, but is far more likely to be the product of a process comparable to the one in which mutations from red to white occur.

The rate of mutations is of the greatest importance for any theory of evolution, as we consider that mutations form the raw material on which evolution works. Methods of determining general mutability are usually very tedious. One might think that it would be possible simply to inspect thousands of plants or animals coming from pure lines and note any abnormalities that were observed, but of course these would then have to be tested to find whether they were inherited or not. In any case, numerical results achieved by this method are unreliable because they are subject to personal errors. Dominants, which are less important from the evolutionary point of view, are much more frequently detected in this way than recessives, as they show in each individual even when they are present in only one of its chromosomes. The same is true of genes localized in that part of the X chromosome which has no homologue in its smaller partner. As was shown in the last chapter, in Drosophila, where the females have two large X chromosomes and the males one X and a smaller Y, all mutant genes localized in the part of the X that has no corresponding part in the Y will always show in the male even if they are recessive, but will be manifest in the female only if they are doubly present. We know that the mutation rate of two autosomal dominants in man, and of hæmophilia which is sex-linked, is about 1:100,000, whereas we know nothing about the mutation rate of autosomal recessives.

The time when a spontaneous mutation must have occurred can sometimes be determined not only in experimental strains of plants or animals, but also in human families whose pedigrees are well known. A famous case was Queen Victoria's. She had no hæmophilic ancestors, but she handed the condition on to the former Russian and Spanish dynasties through her daughters, but not to the reigning English house. Thus the mutation must have arisen in her body or in the gonads of either of her parents.

Certain mutations are much more frequently seen than others and also occur commonly in many species, whereas the rarer ones seem to be confined to one species only: albinism in mammals or the sex-linked yellow body-colour in many species of Drosophila are very probably due to identical mutations. Other more general effects, such as dilution or intensification of fur colour or changes in petal colour, though they may not always be brought about by identical mutations, must have some common features. Back mutations from a pure line of the mutant race to the wild type may or may not be less frequent than the original mutations. Another point is that mutations which cause only slight effects are probably much more frequent than those causing the gross differences which have hitherto formed the main object of the geneticist's research, but this is naturally very difficult to prove.

A different but perhaps even more interesting question arises as to how the mutation rates in different organisms in nature should be compared. It does not make a great deal of difference in a pure line of Drosophila propagated by single pairs whether one says that such and such a mutation occurs once a year or that it occurs once in about thirty-six generations, ten days being the average length of the life-cycle under optimum conditions; but it makes a great difference when the mutation rate in Drosophila is being compared with the mutation rate in man. As we are not usually carrying somatic mutations, and as in fact our children show new dominant mutants only rarely, it is probably correct to assume that the mutation rates are better measured in generations rather than in absolute time. If this is correct, the evolution of a species with a long life-cycle will take much longer than the evolution of short-lived forms. This consideration ought to remind people that most evolutionary processes in man are very slow and that they should be measured by a different time-scale from any that is used in considering social or political progress.

As already indicated, recessives localized in autosomes are not likely to be detected in plants or animals in nature. If we assume that one mutant gene—let us say lack of wings—will be present once in every 10,000 flies of a certain species, the chances of its occurring twice in both chromosomes of an individual are $10,000^2$, or 100,000,000. Clearly nobody has as yet inspected 100,000,000 flies. This assumption holds good only if we also assume that the mating of the flies occurs completely at random in a very great population, in theory an infinite one; and in nature this is never realized. Plants and animals, including man, have a far greater chance of finding mates among the individuals living in the same locality than among those in far-distant regions. The smaller the mating system, the narrower the choice of a mate, and the greater becomes the probability that two recessive genes descending from a mutation in a common ancestor will meet in one individual and show their reunion by the manifestation of the recessive character. The extreme restriction of the mating system is called inbreeding, and it is the most potent method that both the geneticist and the plant- and animal-breeder have for detecting the presence of recessive genes.

We do not know which are the physical causes leading to spontaneous mutation in nature, but it is possible greatly to increase the mutation rate by artificial means. At present the following types of treatment have been found to be effective: irradiation by X-rays, bombardment with neutrons or α-particles, irradiation by ultra-violet light, long exposure to extremely high temperatures, sudden temperature changes and exposure to various chemical substances such as mustard gas or phenol. Of these agents, X-rays have been most used. All these methods are still so crude that they cause not only gene mutations but also breakages of chromosomes and subsequent reunions of various kinds. This is perhaps an indication that there is not necessarily a fundamental difference between the two. The general experience is that it is not possible to get a particular mutation by treating germ-cells with any of these methods with the possible exception of the phenol treatment; one can only make a shot in the dark and detect by subsequent inbreeding, or sometimes by microscopical inspection, what sort of damage has been done by the treatment.

It has already been stated that the action of the gene can most easily be studied when it can be compared with an allele, therefore mutation provides material for the investigation of gene action. It is almost certain that any mutant gene causes numerous alterations in an organism, but usually one of these is outstanding and is the one from which the name of the mutant is derived; but sometimes a gene has several conspicuous effects, and it is then described as having a pleiotropic action. For instance, the same gene may affect a cat, making its fur white and its eyes blue, and also causing it to be deaf, though without any labyrinthine defects. In other mammals conspicuous differences in fur colour may result in slight differences in weight and other quantitative characters. Most of the Drosophila mutants have been shown to possess several effects, even if as a rule only one of them can be used for scoring.

The effects of a mutation on a carrier are not only manifold in their character—the intensity of their manifestation can vary also. In *Drosophila melanogaster* there is a mutant called antenna-less. A strain homozygous for this mutant will contain only a small number of individuals possessing one antenna only or no antennæ in a proportion varying with the cultural conditions. The penetrance, as one says, of this gene is thus a function of the environment; it is probably also controlled by other genes, which in this connection are called modifiers. Different penetrance may also be combined with pleiotropism in such a way that one manifestation always shows, whereas another does not—for example, in man in blue sclerotics the white of the eye is always bluish, owing to the thinness of the sclerotic membrane. Some of the individuals with blue sclerotics have in addition very fragile bones, which lead to multiple fractures and early death. Graded expressivity of genes may show in various ways. There may be a variation in the time of onset of a hereditary disease such as oto-sclerosis. This leads to increasing deafness starting in different individuals at different ages. The intensity of a mutant-controlled colour or the number of structures like hairs, scales, feathers, bristles and vertebræ may also vary with the environment and the presence of modifying genes. The differences in gene action between the homozygous and the heterozygous states have already been described.

CHAPTER XIII

Lethal Mutations and Sterility Factors

It has already been said that most mutations are harmful; individuals carrying a mutant character may grow more slowly or die earlier than the original stocks, while others are more susceptible to noxious environments. The frizzle fowl, for instance, which is a breed characterized by turned-up feathers, is difficult to keep in temperate climates even in the heterozygous form, as the birds very readily die from cold, but in countries like Malaya or West Africa or Jamaica the breed does well and is quite common.

The fact that the effect of a mutation is generally detrimental is easily understood when one considers that all the genes have to act in a sort of harmony to produce a well-balanced organism, and this harmony has been perfected through the generations by selection—that is, by the weeding out of the less fit individuals. A popular comparison would be with a watch. If a part of the mechanism is altered by some chance it is very unlikely that the watch will be improved by the accident.

It can easily be seen that disturbances of various kinds and degrees can be caused by mutations—for instance, the appearance of an animal can be altered in a way which need not affect its functioning very profoundly. More serious may be the slowing down of its development, and even worse is any serious disturbance in the interactions of its vital functions; this may be so serious that no living organism is produced at all. An animal may die as an egg, or during its early development or before it reaches maturity. From the point of view of the population it does not make a great difference at which stage death happens, as long as it occurs before reproduction begins, but to the experimenter these three degrees of disturbance may appear quite different. He calls a genetical factor lethal only when no living offspring is produced, regardless of whether it died early or late in the course of its embryonic development. Factors which cause the death of only a fraction of their carriers and reduce the viability of all of them are called semi-lethals.

In principle, autosomal genes may have a lethal effect if present either singly or in both chromosomes. A gene which is lethal in the heterozygote, however, leads to the death of the first individual which carries it, and is therefore never propagated; but a gene which is lethal only in the homozygous form may be transmitted in the heterozygous stage without much ill effect to the individual. If a population segregating for lethals is inspected at a stage when the non-viable individuals have already disappeared, the lethals can be detected by the absence of a class of offspring which would have been expected to occur. For instance, in an animal species in which the male is the heterozygous sex, a female carrying a recessive lethal in one of her X chromosomes will produce only half of the expected male offspring—that is, the offspring of such a female do not show a sex ratio of round about 1 : 1, but one of roughly one male to two females. Inspection at an earlier stage often reveals the missing individuals—for example, albino seedlings which die in the cotyledon stage, or mouse embryos which are in process of being resorbed.

The position of a lethal in a chromosome can be localized just as exactly as that of any other mutant, although more labour is involved in the procedure and it is too complicated to be described here; but a method to measure lethal production by irradiation may be of interest. Muller has produced a stock of Drosophila which he describes as a *ClB* stock. This is characterized by an X chromosome showing the three following properties: it carries a lethal which does not show in the heterozygous female but prevents all the males that carry it from developing; it carries the dominant mutant gene *Bar*, which produces narrow, kidney-shaped eyes in the heterozygous female, and, lastly, it carries an inversion long enough to prevent most crossing over in the chromosomes. Thus one can be fairly certain that any female showing bar eyes carries the lethal. As all the males carrying *Bar* die, the females have only round-eyed male offspring.

This *ClB* stock can be easily propagated by always selecting females showing the bar character. To test the lethal-producing effect of any agent such as X-rays, males are irradiated and singly mated to *ClB* females. The female offspring of these matings will produce nothing but females if a lethal was produced anywhere in the sex chromosome derived from the treated male. This method is almost foolproof, since it does not depend on the observer's ability to detect special visible characters. After heavy dosages of X-rays up to 20 per cent of the males may develop lethals; but even if untreated males are used, two in 1,000 will show the presence of any of 1,000 or so possible sex-linked lethals. In this way differences can be established in the mutability of various stocks of Drosophila.

Lethals can also be localized in the autosomes, although with greater difficulty. Here again 'trick stocks' have made investigations much easier in some cases—for instance, use can be made of two different lethals which are very close to one another in the same chromosome so that there is practically no crossing over between them. The genes which are lethal in the homozygous condition have visible effects on the phenotype in the heterozygote. An interesting example is found in Drosophila, where the genes dichaete, *D*, and glued, *Gl*, are localized very near to one another in the third chromosome. The names of these lethals are derived from their heterozygous effect, and they are denoted by capital letters because in the heterozygous form they resemble a dominant. It is cumbersome to keep *D* or *Gl* stocks separately, but it is very easy to keep them together as balanced heterozygotes. If two flies of the constitution $\frac{DGl+}{D+Gl}$ are mated zygotes of the constitution $\frac{1}{4}\,\frac{DGl+}{DGl+}$, $\frac{2}{4}\,\frac{DGl+}{D+Gl}$ and $\frac{1}{4}\,\frac{D+Gl}{D+Gl}$ are formed. As the first and the last class are not viable, only half of the flies develop, and these resemble their parents. So the stock of dichæte-glued flies keeps itself balanced through many generations. It is rare for two lethals to be localized so close to each other as are dichæte and glued, but there are also other circumstances which prevent crossing over from happening between two lethals—for example, inversions. It may perhaps be noted that probably many so-called dominant genes causing inborn diseases in man are of the same nature, and if death occurs at an early stage in the homozygote it is never found. Other mutants are sublethal in the homozygous form but comparatively harmless when heterozygous.

Children homozygous for the gene causing Xeroderma pigmentosum, develop a dark and brittle skin at those parts of the body which are exposed to light. Sooner or later malignant growth sets in, and death usually occurs before maturity is reached. Heterozygotes, on the other hand, show only intense freckling, without red hair. Another example is Thalassæmia, a form of anæmia mostly found in Syrian, Greek or Italian families. In the heterozygote it is only a mild disease which sometimes goes unnoticed, whereas the homozygotes invariably seem to die from it.

It has been shown that from the point of view of the species there is no great difference between the effect of a lethal factor and that of any factor which inhibits the propagation of the individual. In addition to lethals there are also mutations decreasing fertility in all degrees up to complete sterility. However, sterility presents a more complicated problem, as it of necessity involves two individuals, and whereas an animal or a plant can in itself show the degree of viability, an individual or a gamete may show different degrees of fertility with different mating partners. In fact intersterility is one of the most important mechanisms in determining the separation of species.

This may originate in many different ways, either by causes acting through the environment or by sudden changes in the gene composition. Mating barriers or chromosome incompatibility can again be of various kinds, which is not surprising as both processes involve a very complicated succession of events. For instance, a Mediterranean squid has two separate races between which the only noticeable difference is their different breeding times, and it has been observed that the females of some races of domestic animals do not attract the males of other races, and so on. Anomalous balance of chromosomes or genes may also cause sterility. It is well known that most hybrids between animal species are sterile, and obviously it is impossible to accomplish an equal distribution of unequal chromosomes, which are sometimes even unequal in number, and balanced nuclei will very seldom result. Sterility factors, often organized in a special form of intersterility mechanism, are well known in many plant species.

CHAPTER XIV

Alleles and Poly-Alleles

IN the preceding chapters the way in which independent and linked genes are inherited has been described; there is, however, another relationship possible between two mutant genes, for they can both be mutants of the same wild-type gene, and then both are localized at homologous places or loci of homologous chromosomes. Such poly-alleles are usually characterized by the fact that they affect the same character or characters—the colour of hair or of feathers, serological properties and various types of colour-blindness are all characters that are determined by the action of poly-alleles.

Some of the eye-colours of Drosophila form a series in which a good deal is known about the alleles controlling them. The wild form has bright-red pigment in its eyes, and among the various known abnormalities there is one series of sex-linked mutations which has already been mentioned, called the white series, in which the eyes may vary through pink and yellowish tinges from red to white. As the first allele of this series to be observed was a white one, all mutants of the series are denoted with w, w^{+} meaning the normal red-eyed, w^{e} meaning eosin, w^{a} meaning apricot and w alone meaning white. The localization of these mutants is indicated in Figure 15. If two alleles which affect the colour in different degrees are combined in a cross the resulting heterozygote offspring, a female, will show an intermediate colour; as the white alleles in Drosophila are sex-linked no combination of two alleles can be observed in a male (compare Figure 18).

The tortoiseshell colouring in cats is due to the presence of alleles in the two sex chromosomes. One of them carries an allele for black and the other an allele for yellow fur colour of part of the coat. As two sex chromosomes in mammals are found only in the female, tortoiseshell tom cats do not exist as a rule. Rare cases have been reported of tortoiseshell toms, but they have never been tested cytologically; probably it would turn out that they were carrying part of a second X chromosome in the nuclei.

In the domestic rabbit, as in many other mammals, pink-eyed albinos with pure white coats are relatively common. The difference between a fully pigmented domestic rabbit and an albino is due to a single gene called a, the pigmented type then being known as a^+. Another mutant exists, called Himalayan, which also has pink eyes, but it is white only on the body, while the legs, ears and forehead are dark, the fur colour being very much as in a Siamese cat. This aberration is also due to a single character denoted by a^h. There are three crosses possible between wild type, albino and Himalayan, apart from the reciprocal crosses: wild type × albino, wild type × Himalayan and Himalayan × albino. The results of these crosses are as follows:

wild type × *albino* gives an F_1 generation of all wild type, and an F_2 of $\frac{3}{4}$ wild and $\frac{1}{4}$ albino,

wild type × *Himalayan* gives an F_1 generation of all wild type, and an F_2 of about $\frac{3}{4}$ wild type and $\frac{1}{4}$ Himalayan,

Himalayan × *albino* gives an F_1 of all Himalayan type, and an F_2 of about $\frac{3}{4}$ Himalayan and $\frac{1}{4}$ albino.

These results are most easily explained by assuming that a^+, the wild type, is dominant over a^h, the Himalayan, which in its turn is dominant over a, the albino, and that all these three characters occur at the same locus. Figure 22 shows a very simple way of demonstrating this relationship.

It is very likely that among the minute aberrations of gene structure poly-alleles are much more frequent than among the more spectacular mutations; if so they would provide a reservoir for genetical reorganization of the species. Such

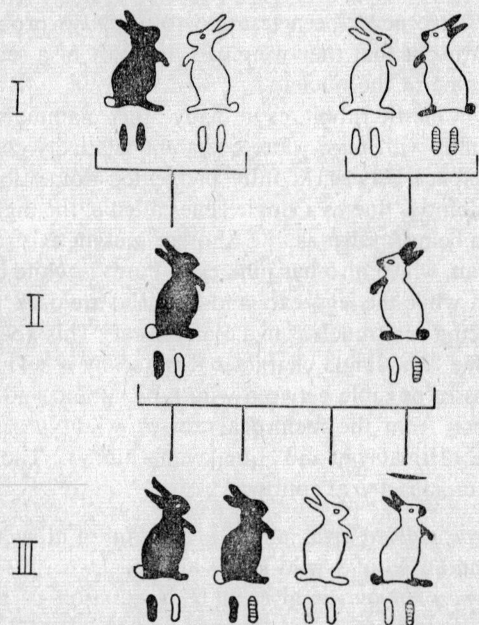

FIG. 22.—Cross of the offspring from a wild type and an albino rabbit, and from an albino and a Himalayan rabbit. The result in the third generation shows that albino and Himalayan are mutants localized at the same locus (*i.e.*, poly-alleles), that wild type is dominant over both mutants, and that Himalayan is dominant over albino.

arrangements are necessary if one gene effecting a major change in organization—for instance, a gene making for dark body-colour—becomes dominant to the wild-type paler gene after a period when it has spread in the population as a recessive. Such a change of dominance between two alleles can be explained most easily on the assumption that other genes forming the background, or genetical environment, for the black and the original wild-type genes change in their combination. This in turn presupposes the permanent existence of a number of alleles. A wild population, therefore, must usually be regarded as heterozygous in many respects, even if the appearance of the individuals does not betray the fact.

CHAPTER XV

In the Flower Garden

ALTHOUGH nowadays all sorts of varieties of colours are found in the same species of flower, in earlier times each one had its own distinctive colour. In some cases the colours actually took their names from the flowers—thus violet was the colour of violets, and rose was the colour of the original red rose. How did the variation in colour arise?

Many flowers are pollinated by insects—bees, flies and moths are all instrumental in carrying pollen. These insects see colours differently from human beings, but they can nevertheless get used to a particular colour, and a bee, for instance, which has collected nectar for some time from a blue sage is then attracted by the blue colour, and tends to pay no attention to a yellow snapdragon. Therefore in the past plants which happened to produce flowers of widely different colours were less successful in getting the bees to fertilize them. However, as soon as the domestication of plants began and man, or rather woman, began to keep flowers in the neighbourhood of houses, this state of affairs was interfered with, and any flower of an unusual colour tended to be picked out and saved for seed. This pleasure in new and fancy forms persists to-day, as may be seen from the number of societies that are devoted to the cultivation of different kinds of plants.

A garden plant—the common pea *Pisum sativum*—was the first living thing in which the laws of heredity were detected. In 1865 Gregor Mendel described characters in this plant which were inherited in a simple way. The characters he studied first were not the colours of the flowers, but were concerned with properties of the plant as a whole and with those of the seeds. For instance, he took tall and dwarf plants, plants with the flowers born in the axils of the leaves or on the ends, plants in which the seeds were light green, dark green or yellow, or where they were round and smooth or angular and wrinkled. Of greater interest to the flower-gardener is the sweet pea, *Lathyrus odoratus.* The wild form of this species probably came from Sicily originally, and was first introduced into England in 1699. The flowers had reddish-purple standards with light bluish-purple wings, and the offspring of sweet peas of very different colours frequently have flowers of the wild type. The variety and beauty of cultivated sweet peas are very great indeed—there are red and scarlet flowers, white and almost black, hooded and picotee, and many others, but as the sweet pea is usually self-pollinated in England, because pollination occurs before the flower opens, it is not suitable for amateur breeding experiments.

Flowers can be divided into three colour classes—white, yellow, and the range from red to blue. These colours can be intensified or diluted, and in the third class an increase in redness or blueness of tone can occur. In some plants two or three of these colour classes can be found combined, but the colours of the three groups are produced in very different ways. Whiteness is due to the structure of the petals, which in the absence of pigment causes part of the light to be reflected from the many cell walls of the tissues, just as the whiteness of snow is caused by the reflection of light. The yellow colours, ranging from yellow to orange, are mostly brought about by the presence of the organic substances xanthophyll or carotene. These are highly complex compounds occurring in the plastids of the epidermis of the petals. These plastids are inclusions of the plasma, which can also be colourless, and which in the cells of the leaves are green. Loss of the plastid colour in a yellow flower results in a white variety, while an alteration in the nature of the plastid pigment can lead to the intensification of its colour, so that yellow can become orange.

Apart from the flavons which give their yellow colour to roses and primroses and some other flowers, the only colouring substances dissolved in the cell-sap are the anthocyanins, which are the blue-red pigments. It is known that an increase in the blueness of a flower can occur in several ways; the most common is by the production of a co-pigment, which interacts with anthocyanin. More rarely it is brought about by making the tissues of the petal more alkaline. If a purple sweet pea is put on top of an ammonia bottle the vapour will make the colour change violently towards blue or even to green, and the wings and keel, which previously appeared to be of the same colour, assume quite different colours. The same sort of changes also occur when flowers wither. Different shades of blueness in flowers are also produced by a series of different anthocyanins which are of slightly different compositions; a series exists in which the pigments are called pelargonidin, cyanidin and delphinidin, the first one being the reddest. Many of these differences in colour and chemical composition are due to differences in single genes.

Snapdragons and wallflowers are suitable flowers for experiments on the inheritance of flower colour. Snapdragons are found in a very wide range of colours, most of which are due to differences in single genes. The wallflower is rather less favourable for experimentation because in England it is a biennial plant. It may have flowers with fully yellow plastids or paler lemon yellow, and there are also flowers with and without various types of anthocyanin; finally there may be flowers with no pigments at all—so white, yellow, orange, brown, pink and purple wallflowers may be achieved. In addition, there are characters affecting the size of the plant, the colour of the leaves and the shape of the flowers, all of which can be used for genetical experiments.

The Chinese primrose, *Primula sinensis*, affords another interesting genetical study. The plant was brought to England in 1819 and again in 1826, and it is believed that no later importation has taken place. It occurs in diploid and tetraploid races with twenty-four and forty-eight chromosomes respectively, the tetraploid plants being larger, especially as far as the flowers are concerned. The tetraploid race is called *gigas*. Diploids will breed with diploids, and tetraploids with tetraploids, although not quite so effectively, but the two forms can be crossed only with great difficulty. Of the twelve possible linkage groups, only six are so far represented by more than one (2–6) mutant gene; altogether more than twenty mutant genes have been investigated. They affect the colour of the various parts of the flower, transform anthers into petals (doubling) and produce various leaf-forms and general habits such as the rosetted habit. All the English commercial varieties of *Primula sinensis* are pin—that is, they have a long stigma and short anthers. Thrum flowers have been bred in Germany. These have long anthers and a short stigma. This difference is also due to a gene or a gene complex. *Primula sinensis* flowers from January to May, and February is the best month for pollination. The flowers used as females need not be protected from insects after emasculation, which, however, must be carried out before the anthers burst. Pollination is best done by hand, but fingers and forceps must be dipped into alcohol every time a different pollen is used.

In garden plants one can often observe other curious phenomena. Roses are found which bear flowers of three different types on one bush; some branches have flowers of the ordinary rose colour, others have very bright scarlet flowers, while there are some flowers which show both colours, and frequently one petal even may be divided, and one-half will be rose and the other scarlet. As the border line between the two different colours is a radius if the whole flower is regarded as a circle, and so marks the division between two sectors, such occurrences are called sectorial chimæras. They are also found in other flowers. They originate in disarrangements of the chromosome structure known as somatic mutations (see page 92), and may be caused by the loss of a whole chromosome; usually, however, they are due to multi-mutating genes. In the case of such a rose-bush the same gene must have mutated several times in different cells, which indicates that great instability may be found in the gene constitution of some plants.

The majority of garden plants can be obtained in many varieties from growers, and in many species the differences in colour, shape and other characters are due to one or two mutant genes; but commercial seeds are very rarely completely homogeneous and even less frequently are they true breeding. This is owing to the difficulty of carrying out artificial pollination on a large scale, and to the fact that insect pollination or wind pollination can never be completely reliable.

CHAPTER XVI

Spreading of Genes in Populations

It has been shown that gene mutations do occur with a certain frequency, although they are comparatively rare events, and that there are several methods for determining such frequencies. The fate of these mutants is determined by many factors, several of which will now be discussed. The frequency itself is one very important factor; another is the size of the population and a third is the rate of reproduction. If we imagine an insect pair producing 1,000 offspring per year, mutations occurring with a frequency of 1 in 500 would seem to have very little chance of being carried on to the next generation, the probability in each case being only 1 in 500.* However, when we consider that insect populations are usually very numerous, this rare event will happen in quite a number of matings, and if the gene is not too disadvantageous it will spread. On the other hand, in man, who produces only a very few children, of whom the majority, however, grow up and propagate, almost any non-lethal mutation has a good chance of being carried on, whether the mating system be large or small; but of course it may get lost in the next generation. In small mating systems, representing either an entire species or an isolated part of one, mutants will get lost more easily than in large populations, and this will result in a loss of genetical variability in these groups.

It thus appears that in the first period of the establishment

* This follows from the fact that as the number of individuals in a species does not alter much from year to year only two out of the 1,000 will on the average reach maturity.

of a new gene chance plays a much greater part than fitness. In this way we can explain the fact that even genes which are slightly disadvantageous may spread a little if they originate often enough by mutation, but once a mutation has spread to any extent selection begins to become effective. Autosomal mutants will then be found much more frequently in the heterozygous form than as homozygotes. Consequently selection will take place between the heterozygote and the wild type rather than between the homozygotes.

In experiments where it is possible to increase the number of mutants by inbreeding the viability can be measured by the percentage of homozygotes produced in the offspring from a cross or after several generations; but even under these conditions selection of the heterozygotes is usually more effective than selection of the homozygotes. It has already been pointed out that most mutants tend to reduce viability, but at the same time reduced fitness for one habitat may mean an increased fitness for a neighbouring one, and consequently carriers of mutant genes acting in this direction can be considered as preadapted to a new environment. They then may be expected, and have indeed been observed, to invade new areas which were not formerly inhabited by the species.

The degree of selective pressure on a mutant is also dependent on the chromosome in which it lies, its dominance and other properties. A gene localized in a sex chromosome will always show in the heterozygous sex, whether it is recessive or dominant; it will be more quickly eliminated than a recessive autosomal gene, as the latter type can spread considerably before an individual will have it in both homologous chromosomes, and so show the recessive character, together with its possibly detrimental effects. A dominant gene, even if autosomal, will always affect every individual carrying it, and thus be even more quickly eliminated than a sex-linked one. Of course intermediate genes will show different degrees of selective pressure, usually a smaller difference for heterozygotes and a bigger difference for homozygotes, according to the degree with which the character or characters determining the viability are manifest in these two genetical types (see also page 100). Another type of balance is reached when selection favours the heterozygotes, as often happens in polymorphic species—that is, species whose members fall into distinct groups differing in appearance. In such a condition no type can supersede the other, because the heterozygotes, being more viable, produce the greatest number of offspring, and these will include all the types—namely, the heterozygotes and both homozygotes, and an equilibrium will develop where all these phenotypes are present. It is worth mentioning that viability is not in all cases associated with the visible character. Though the visible character may be recessive, viability may be decreased or increased already in the heterozygote. The increase of viability in organisms heterozygous for many genes has long been known to plant- and animal-breeders as hybrid vigour. It is gradually lost after inbreeding from the F_1 generation.

The spreading and distribution of mutant genes in a population have the greatest bearing on the evolution of all species, including man. The changes which occur, which may or may not lead to equilibria, are determined by the rate and selective value of the mutations and by the size and movements of the population. As in all statistical matters, assumptions have to be made which, although they are of apparent simplicity, are never completely realized in nature, and therefore have to be modified later on. For instance, one can make deductions from the four following assumptions. First there may be two alleles, *Bb*, which are stable, which means mutations are so rare that they can be disregarded. Secondly, the three possible genotypes, *BB*, *Bb*, *bb*, will give the same number of offspring if mated in any combination. Thirdly, the population is infinitely large, and, fourthly, any male is as likely to mate with any female in the whole population as with any other. Before arriving at any deductions, it must be pointed out that such a state of affairs is never realized in nature—for instance, the third and fourth conditions are contradictory. It is impossible in an infinitely large population, and even in a very large one, that all males will have the same chance to mate with any particular female, simply because of the spatial extension of the species. To take a human example, it is much more likely that two Londoners will marry than that a Londoner will marry a New Yorker. Further, the only conceivable thing which can lead to the appearance of the alleles *Bb* is mutation, and therefore mutations cannot be disregarded. Finally it will very seldom happen that the three genotypes are equally viable and fertile. Nevertheless the formula which can be deduced from the four statements is a very useful one, as we shall show later on.

Let us assume that the gene *B* is four times as frequent as *b*, and let the frequency of *B* be p. We assess p as 0·8, which means that if we could inspect a very great number of chromosomes and were able to see a genetic difference in the locus of p, which we are not, we should find 80 per cent chromosomes with the gene *B* (a frequency of 0·8.) Consequently the chromosomes carrying *b* must occur at a frequency of 1—0·8, which is 0·2. This frequency we call q, which means that $p + q$ must equal 1—that is, they comprise the whole population. If we want to know the relative frequency of the phenotypes *BB*, *Bb* and *bb* in the population we can find it from the chequer diagram on page 117.

If we had inserted p and q in this diagram we should have got the proportion for the phenotypes as p^2 *BB*: $2pq$ *Bb*: q^2 *bb*. The formula represents not only equilibrium persist-

	0·8 *B*	0·2 *b*
0·8 *B*	0·64 *BB*	0·16 *Bb*
0·2 *b*	0·16 *Bb*	0·04 *bb*

ing as long as conditions remain valid, but, as in all chequer-board diagrams of a similar type, it also indicates the frequencies of phenotypes of a mixture in the first generation—in fact, if it is compared with the diagram on page 57, it will be found that it is merely an extension of the 1 : 2 : 1 segregation modified by p and q, which do not indicate anything but the relative numbers of the types chosen for the mixture. By reversal of this formula one can find the relative frequency of alleles in a population from the relative numbers of the phenotypes. Examples of this will be found in the chapter about human genetics and blood groups (page 147). Similar formulæ can be derived for sex-linked genes or for more complicated relationships such as the presence of more than two alleles. As mentioned above, a recessive sex-linked gene will always show when it is present in the heterozygous sex, which is the male in man or the hen in poultry, whereas in the homozygous sex it will show only in the homozygous form. If a large population is searched for some character—for instance, a certain type of colour-blindness such as red–green blindness—it may be found that the number of men showing it according to some standards is about 3 per cent. The number of women showing it is about 0·09 per cent, therefore it is fairly likely that one man of every reader's acquaintance will be red–green blind, but quite unlikely that one of the women will be. If the formula is applied it is at once seen that the proportion of red–green-blind men—namely, 3 in 100—is about the square root of the proportion of the colour-blind women 9 in 10,000, and it is therefore concluded that red–green blindness in man is a sex-linked gene; its frequency in the male population is 3 per cent, and its frequency in the female population in the heterozygous state is also 3 per cent and in the homozygous state 0·09 per cent. In fact, this is borne out by the study of family pedigrees.

Mutant genes have frequently been observed spreading (increasing) in populations, or they have been found in some sort of equilibrium with their wild-type allelomorphs. Among the few populations where the decrease of a mutant has been observed are the silver foxes of some northern regions of Canada; here foxes have been shot and trapped for over a century and record books were kept at various stations—for instance, by some Moravian missionaries. The species in question resembles the red fox of the old world to some extent in appearance, and most of the skins recorded were ordinary red-fox skins, but there were also aberrant animals of two types: silver foxes having rather dark furs with white tips, and cross foxes, which were between the normal and the silver fox, but rather reddish and on the whole more similar to the wild type. All the evidence shows that the silver fox is homozygous for one mutant gene, whereas the cross fox is heterozygous for the same gene. The furs registered in one year are not unselected samples of the population; about four times as much is paid for a silver fox as for a red fox, so the hunters would always kill proportionately more of the silver foxes by shooting, though this would not be so if trapping alone were done. It is difficult for the hunter to distinguish the heterozygous cross fox from the wild type, and therefore this type would not be affected by selective shooting. In spite of the hunter's bias, the lists give good evidence of the decrease in the percentage of silver and cross foxes; for instance, the percentage of silver fox has decreased since 1840 from between 11 and

18 per cent in different areas to from 4 to 6 per cent in the same regions, which seems quite a significant decline. The total number of furs, on the other hand, has not declined in the same way, although it is subject to violent fluctuations of a complicated periodicity, of which the most striking element is a four-year cycle probably depending on the abundance of rodents on which the foxes live. This periodic reduction of a large population to a very small one may be quite important in aiding the effect of selective shooting. Of course it is conceivable that other factors than female fashion have affected the percentage of silver foxes, but we do not know what they are, and the habitat has not altered very much during the century in question. The breeding of silver foxes, which has certainly decreased the market value of the skins, started too late to affect the result, but it may show in the future.

CHAPTER XVII

Adaptation of the Species

ANIMALS and plants are usually adapted to their environments—that is, they can live in them successfully and produce sufficient offspring to replace the parents when they die—fossils, however, show that in the past there have been many other species of plants and animals which are no longer in existence. It is clear that these forms must have disappeared in one of the following ways: either all the individuals died out as conditions changed—which is probably true of the majority—or the species changed in such a way as to comply with the new conditions. Several instances are known where science thinks it has found a more or less complete series of such alterations—for instance, the long line of horses starting from five-fingered, rabbit-like forms and ending with the present-day horses and donkeys, or the many marvellous series of ammonites.

The environmental conditions which may by their changes induce a species transformation are manifold; the distribution of lands and seas, mountains and plains has changed during the geological period, and so has climate. Usually such changes occur gradually, and the span of man's life is rarely sufficient to notice great changes in the animals and plants which are subjected to them; but some natural changes are rather fast, and volcanic events, such as the formation of new islands, or the destruction of the whole flora and fauna of an island, or changes of a river's bed, all happen quickly. Studies of plant and animal life in these circumstances have proved very illuminating.

At present the most potent factor which is changing the

conditions of life is probably man's activity. The oceans are in large areas covered with oil, which greatly interferes with bird life, the air is full of smoke and soot, causing industrial melanism of moths, the vegetation of vast territories is changed by agriculture and forestry, and with the vegetation the fauna has also changed completely. Not only the large cities and industrial regions but also village greens, parks and artificial pools constitute completely new habitats for many organisms. Quite apart from directly influencing the frequency of species by favouring the useful and suppressing the noxious, man also affects the flora and fauna involuntarily. Therefore cultivated types of formerly wild animals and plants provide the best examples of adaptation and of the adaptability of species.

Usually an animal or a plant is best adapted to its natural habitat, and if it is transplanted to another it perishes or does less well, but there are exceptions. First of all man, who indeed is one of the most ubiquitous animals on earth, has sometimes done better in newly settled regions—for instance, in the United States of America—than in the old countries, and several other immigrant species, which have been brought by settlers into their new countries, have become much more successful in the new environment, at least for some time. In this way the marsupials of Australia have been to some extent replaced by imported European mammals; whole islands have been covered with cactus, and dandelions—the white man's plant as the Red Indians call them—have followed the new railways all over the United States. Insect pests have sometimes proved extremely disastrous in fresh places, and so have micro-organisms and viruses, causing various epidemic diseases both of man and of animals.

Whether the progress of a species into wide regions is spectacular or not, any new environment demands adaptations. The most natural assumption would be that the individuals get adapted, either at once or gradually through the generations, and that their constitution is transmitted to their offspring. The belief in the inheritance of acquired characters, which is often called Lamarckism, after a French zoologist of the eighteenth century, has nowadays been given up by most biologists, for reasons that any reader of this book will easily understand. Genes do not often mutate, but rather go on producing genes of the same constitution, and, if they do change, the direction of their mutation does not seem to be correlated with any special requirements of their environment and is more frequently harmful than advantageous. Therefore most biologists are inclined to regard evolution as an adaptive process composed essentially of two elements, both of them being subject to selection by the environment: variability, caused by the mutation of individual genes, and fresh re-combinations of genes. As long as an environment remains the same a genetical equilibrium is maintained, and new mutants will not easily establish themselves unless they improve upon the viability of the organism, nor will new gene combinations oust the old ones; but if the conditions of life change, mutants and gene combinations which so far have been eliminated can become favourable and may be established in the population. In this way a species would adapt itself to the environment. Many biologists think that the perpetual reshuffling of mutants by means of fertilization and meiosis has its main effect in the maintenance of a perpetual variability and recombination of genes which enables the species to adapt itself to the changing world.

As examples of adaptability the following may serve. In some hot springs in Iceland and elsewhere insects are found living at temperatures up to 70° C., at which degree of heat protein normally coagulates and life become impossible. As other insects die at such high temperatures, it is reasonable to assume that the inhabitants of the hot springs have gradually become adapted, probably by penetrating from the cooler brook which is fed by the spring. Surprisingly, it is possible to imitate this adaptation by breeding insects at higher and higher temperatures through several generations; although one does not reach quite such extremes, cultures can be bred which will flourish at temperatures where the ancestral forms would have died and where offspring which have been kept at normal temperatures in parallel cultures also perish. Similar effects can be obtained with Infusoria and flagellates. At present little is known about the mechanism of these adaptations, whether they are affected genetically or wholly by regulation of the individuals.

Another important adaptation is that of marine animals to fresh water and vice versa. For instance, Crustacea are found in fresh-water lakes, though their relatives occur only in salt water; the shrimp Mysis is an example of this. Industrial melanism, which has already been mentioned, is a very impressive adaptational process. Many Lepidoptera which previously have been represented by light-coloured wild types are supplanted by dark forms about eighty years after a region has become industrialized or urbanized. This phenomenon, which was first observed in England, has now been reported from France, Germany, Belgium, Central Europe, the United States and the Soviet Union. It is still not fully explained, but it is possible that darker forms show a greater resistance to some of the agents in the industrial atmosphere and the contaminated vegetation. Thus, although they are at a disadvantage in an unspoiled environment, the greater hardiness of the black forms in an industrial region would be a decisive factor in selection. The advantage of the black insects may be of a very different character: they may be less obvious when they are on the sooty plants to birds which prey upon them than when sitting on a fresh leaf; they may be more resistant to desiccation, and so able to keep alive longer searching for their food-plants, which may be rarer in these regions than elsewhere. Experiments have shown that there is some justification for all these theories and for several others in addition. Therefore we may conclude that the process of adaptation, although it is of the greatest importance and is constantly happening, is a very difficult subject to study, and so far its explanation has for the most part eluded scientists, but with increasing knowledge its mechanism will be elucidated in many instances during the next decades.

To give some idea of how selection would act upon a population, the development of dominance will be considered. It has already been mentioned that many mutant genes seem to be recessive when they first appear, which means that their counterparts—the wild-type genes—are dominant. This one would not expect *a priori*, as any hypothesis ascribing chemical properties to the genes might easily yield some kind of intermediate effect in the heterozygote. Closer investigation of a number of heterozygotes would probably reveal that many of them are not really of identical phenotype with the wild type, but in any case they are very much nearer to it than to the homozygous mutant. Now, it is a curious fact that if a recessive mutant becomes established in a population it very often also becomes dominant—that is at least what is generally assumed. It would seem difficult to explain the change of dominance by a change in the mutated gene proper—for instance, by a change in its chemical constitution—as this would mean a fresh mutation. However, such a situation has been found in some cotton species. Mostly the cause of the change of dominance is in the gene's environment, and in particular in what is called its genetical background, which is nothing but the sum of all the other genes in the chromosome set.

Several examples have been described in the fowl, where genes dominant in the domestic race become recessive by continued outcrossing into an otherwise wild-type background. It has been mentioned that a recessive gene will occur in many more individuals single than double, therefore the selective agents will act much more efficiently on the heterozygotes than on the homozygotes. Now, as the wild type can be considered almost invariably as better adapted to its environment than the mutant, the heterozygous individuals, which are more similar to the wild type, would appear to be favoured before those which more closely resemble the homozygous mutant. In this way a low expressivity of the mutant gene is selected; as long as this goes on the heterozygotes will become more and more similar to the wild type, and the dominance of the wild type would be explained. On the other hand, if the mutant gene becomes more advantageous for its carriers, the other genes, which in this context are called modifying genes, will be selected the other way round, and in this way the change of dominance will be expected at about the same time as, or a little later than, the mutant gene reaches a higher frequency in a population than the old wild-type gene. It should be pointed out that the selection of fresh assortments of the 'modifying genes' does not depend on the occurrence of mutations among them after the mutation of the 'main gene' has taken place, but that it can draw on the store of mutants present as a consequence of the heterozygosy of most populations.

This theory can explain rather well the frequent occurrence of numerous recessives in wild populations. Obviously as long as there is not much inbreeding heterozygotes which are little different in phenotype from the wild type will not be at a great disadvantage, and will spread the recessive gene in the population. If many recessives are spread in this way the whole population will become heterozygous for one or several factors, and if inbreeding from a fertilized female of such a population is started, numerous recessives will appear. The theory does not apply to sex-linked factors.

An interesting situation arises when two species are concerned in mutual adaptation—*e.g.*, a host and its parasite. Many parasites, such as fungi, bacteria, viruses or small animals, have a shorter life-cycle than their hosts, and are consequently quicker in adapting themselves to altered conditions. Thus any move on the part of the host will be quickly countered by a change in the gene composition of the parasitic population. A consequence of this is the regular appearance of resistant strains of micro-organisms in man and animals, and of insect pests on plants, which after some time often invalidate a chemical method of control which at first proved to be very effective.

The heterozygous composition of populations is not only important for any theory of evolution in the natural adaptation of the species, but also provides the raw material for the selecting activities of the breeder; indeed, the possibility of separating significantly different pure lines from a common ancestry can only be understood in view of the latter's heterozygous gene constitution.

CHAPTER XVIII

The Evolutionary Importance of Recombinations

It is true that mutations provide the hereditary variation on which selection works and that this dual process constitutes evolution, but in this simplified story one aspect has been neglected—namely, the time which has enabled a species to accumulate alleles. Let us consider autosomal recessives. Such mutants are usually harmful in the homozygous state, and are therefore quickly eliminated, and an equilibrium is established mainly between the wild type and the heterozygotes, which often look very similar. As in large breeding communities heterozygous will be much more frequent than homozygous recessives, new mutants will be checked by selection, operating first on the heterozygotes and later more radically on the homozygotes. In this way many loci will be represented in a wild population by various alleles in varying proportions, and provided mutation rate and environment keep constant for a long time, some sort of uneasy equilibrium between all these genes will be reached. This whole complicated system, which also is adapted to the interactions of the genes, can then be called genetically adapted, and it will be reasonably stable. Now let us assume that conditions change. Obviously such a complicated system offers many more possibilities of regulation and a much faster adaptability to any change in the environment than a genetically homogeneous population, which could change only as a consequence of current mutation. If, for instance, by way of simplifying matters, we assume that in the changed circumstances one particular mutant gene would be more favourable than the wild-type allele which was established under the old conditions, a change-over can clearly occur much faster if this mutant is already spread over the whole population than if selection can work only on the rare individuals where mutation has just taken place. The difference between the two situations may perhaps be visualized by comparing the production of mutations with a stream. The production of mutations at a certain rate would correspond to the amount of water carried by the stream in a certain time, and selection, in the absence of heterozygosy, would work only on this rather small volume. Heterozygosy, on the other hand, may be compared with a lake in the course of the stream, and selection can then ladle out of the great volume of variability stored in this lake. It is obvious that this analogy should not be pressed too far.

Genetical diversity is clearly dependent on the size of the population. The smallest unit is the mating group, which may be part of a larger population, as is the case with wind-pollinated plants, or identical with an isolated population—for example, snail populations in neighbouring valleys. The mating systems not only get to be different from the bulk of the species, but they also become less adaptable, and owing to closer inbreeding they frequently die out. Their habitats are often repopulated by descendants from the bulk of the species, whether mating barriers have arisen or not.

If there are many heterozygotes of one type in a human population the recessive genes will frequently become homozygous, and therefore manifest; if the heterozygotes are rare, the homozygous recessives will occur more frequently among the offspring of related people than they do in the general population. If the recessives are harmful, the process is known as degenerative inbreeding. In this respect a very curious situation prevails. Religious or national minorities, as well as populations of places far from modern traffic, tend to inbreeding. Recessive genes in such groups become more frequently manifest than elsewhere, whether they are indifferent, as is red hair among Jews, Irishmen and gypsies, or most deleterious, as are some rare defects, or even advantageous, as was the case in the offspring from the mutineers of the *Bounty*. At the same time the deleterious genes are slightly less frequent in the groups mentioned than in the general population, because, as they occur more frequently in the homozygous state, they are also more frequently eliminated than if they meet more rarely in an outbreeding system. If therefore a member of such a group marries a member either of another group or of the general population, the likelihood that the offspring will be affected by the recessive anomaly will be smaller than in either the general population or in his original group.

At the present time inbreeding is decreasing and outbreeding increasing, and the consequence of this will be that harmful recessives will spread throughout humanity; but the incidence of the inborn diseases due to these factors will diminish as long as this expansion of the mating system continues. Therefore at present most of the severe measures of negative eugenics would seem to be superfluous; but should humanity for any reason be broken up into smaller mating communities, the spreading of these recessives would at once become manifest in a marked increase of the incidence of inborn diseases. However, as such a development is very unlikely, and would in any case mean the end of our civilization, genetical considerations in such circumstances would probably not be important. Alternatively, it must be expected that the greater mating groups will also in some distant future become saturated with recessives and that an equilibrium at a new but similar level will be reached.

The importance of latent variability becomes manifest from another aspect, too. Usually in arguments about the mechanism of selection sufficient distinction is not drawn between units transmitting hereditary characters—principally genes or chromosomes—and the units on which selection mostly works—that is, principally individuals or groups of individuals. An organism is not merely a sum of independent genetical factors, and a gene does not affect only one character; consequently an organism is the product of the interaction of all its genetical factors with themselves and with the individual's environment. It has already been said that in different environments, or after environmental changes, different combinations of genes become more advantageous, and therefore are selected; but this also does apply to various genetical combinations; as an example, the adaptation of two markedly differing alleles will be considered. It has long been observed that many mutants, which at first were very well marked in breeding experiments, became less and less distinguishable in the course of generations, in spite of the fact that they were usually selected by the breeder according to their markedness. For instance, a black mutant of an insect may become less and less black, and in the end almost indistinguishable from the original wild type. However, if such animals are crossed to the wild type, the mutant will show quite clearly in the offspring. Similar effects have been obtained by crossing various strains of the domestic fowl with the wild ancestral form. Such results are conceivable only if a store of modifying genes is present in a population. The selection there has acted upon these modifiers. The developments described are best explained by a change of dominance.

CHAPTER XIX

Some Economic Aspects of Genetics – Breeding

WHILE unconscious selection has helped man since prehistoric times to improve his livestock and crops, with the development of civilization breeding became part of the agriculturalist's rational effort to increase the yield and change the performance of the animals and plants which made up his community. If a man has a particularly good sheep-dog, or a very strong horse, or a cow producing much more milk than his neighbour's, the latter will try to buy it or to get permission to breed from it. This certainly must have happened in very early times. The development of town and Court life gave impetus to the breeding of many various stocks, partly to keep pace with the more varied activities that had arisen, such as hunting and racing, partly just for the pleasure of having fancy forms. In this way race-horses were separated from utility horses, the various breeds of dogs developed, gold-fish and ducks were bred and flower-gardening began.

It is rather remarkable that until recently there was a much closer relationship between fancy breeding and genetics than there is between economic breeding and genetics, and in the most reactionary States, as well as in Russia, one still finds many breeders, and even scientists, who deny the practical uses of Mendelism. However, it is easy to see why this is so. It has already been shown that gross aberrations are due to sudden changes in single genes, and, since the proper working of an organism depends on a rather precarious balance between all its genes, it is not surprising that gross isolated changes in one of the factors usually produce an organism which is inferior in fitness, and would therefore never be selected by the breeder. What the economic breeder selects are efficient combinations of many genes, which singly would have a slight effect only, but which together increase power, speed, milk, meat and so on. The analysis of such combinations controlling quantitative characters is very difficult and not yet well developed, and breeders have had to rely upon rather arbitrary plans of breeding to improve their stocks in these economic respects. On the other hand, qualitative and conspicuous changes, such as the production of white horses, spotted cows or bearded wheat, which are frequently controlled by single genes, are of little direct economic importance; but these are the characters that have been scientifically investigated. In fancy breeding the most spectacular changes of a qualitative nature are the most likely to be perpetuated, and no attention is paid to whether the affected animals or plants are less viable than the wild types. The greatest trouble is taken to breed bulldogs, or telescope eyes in fish, double begonias, or even blue roses, even if such forms can be produced or maintained only with the greatest difficulty. The heredity of many of these spectacular mutants was easily traced by the geneticist, and it is not surprising that he first concentrated on such material. It is in this way that all the important facts of heredity have been established, beginning with Mendel's laws and coming down to almost everything contained in this book. At present polygenic inheritance is being investigated by some geneticists, and there are good prospects of plant and animal breeding soon profiting as a result of their work. Great practical contributions have been made by geneticists, especially in the breeding of plants, as plants much more than animals are inclined to become polyploid, and many of the cereals, fruits and vegetables are polyploid, usually auto-polyploids. There are new methods now of producing such forms almost at will—for instance, it can be done by cutting shoots and then propagating vegetatively from the tetraploid tissue, which often develops from the wound, or by elaborate forms of grafting. If a plant alkaloid called colchicine, which is produced by the autumn crocus, is applied to the wound, even more of the regenerated parts of the plant will become polyploid, usually tetraploid; and what is even more remarkable is that such plants sometimes propagate sexually without becoming diploid again, and even if they do not give tetraploid seeds they can be propagated vegetatively. The colchicine method has so far given us stronger plants and bigger garden flowers—for instance, Portulacca, Phlox, Petunia, Digitalis, Tropæolum, Cheiranthus and numerous others. Colchicine also helped to make fertile an important cross of two tobacco species, *Nicotiana tabacum* and *Nicotiana glutinosa*, by forming allo-polyploids. There is evidence that a doubling of the chromosomes may change sterile forms to fertile, a diœcious to an hermaphrodite race or an annual to a perennial.

Some of the hereditary differences that are due to single genes are also of direct economic value. In the maize plant there is a mutant which causes the deposit of sugar in the corn instead of a part of the usual starch, and this sweet corn is better for use as a vegetable than ordinary maize.

Quite a different use of the laws of inheritance can be made by poultry-keepers: the sexing of poultry is commercially important, as pullets for egg-laying are wanted in most places, while cockerels are either killed or sent to separate places to be fattened as table birds. Although some Japanese specialists and other experts are able to sex a newly hatched chicken of any race by inspecting sex papillæ, it is considered by most people to be a difficult art, and the results, in any case, are not very reliable. Sexing by means of a sex-linked character, most often one affecting the plumage, is therefore widely used. Bearing in mind that the female is the heterogametic sex in birds, differences between early or late feathering strains can be used to distinguish male and female, or gold down-colour against silver down-colour, or dark heads against light heads. Finally the sex linkage can be made use of in breeding from any barred variety, provided that the down-colours are uniform.

In some tropical breeds of cattle a so-called temperamental character affecting the letting down of the milk is found which may be inherited. This is a reflex to suckling or stroking the teats, but in some breeds—for instance, in Jamaica and Trinidad—it will work only in the presence of the calf. This primitive behaviour was probably quite common formerly, for on Babylonian friezes calves are to be seen tied to the necks of their mothers, but nowadays a more docile temperament is found in our dairy cows. Similar tameness factors probably also occur in mice and rats.

In breeding domestic animals for particular purposes use is made of differences in speed of growth and proportions of different parts of the body at various stages during development; these are dependent on many factors. In the horse, for instance, the relative length of the legs is increased during fœtal life; therefore if early growth is increased faster horses will result. Weight and thickness of bones and muscles, on the other hand, increase mainly after birth, therefore draught horses will result from the selection of strains showing strong post-natal growth.

In the pig body-shape and composition are particularly plastic, and can be transformed greatly by genetic and environmental factors. Here again a selection of body proportions differing greatly from those of the wild ancestor has led to great increases in yield. Strains exist which are kept for fat production because they mature and grow fat early. These are best fed abundantly and slaughtered early; slow maturing strains kept on a low diet produce more lean and less fat. In sheep also environmental and genetical factors must be combined to produce good mutton or good wool, and use is also made of differential growth in this species. It is not generally known that the fine texture of the wool of the Merino sheep is not only controlled by the inherited characters of the breed, but is also due to partial starvation.

The methods of improving livestock will to a great extent depend on the fertility of the species concerned. In poultry and in pigs, where the progeny are numerous and reproduction is fast, it is possible to start and breed from scratch by buying eggs or boars and sows. In cattle, sheep and horses, however, which normally produce one offspring only in a season, improvement of stock can as a rule not be effected by replacement by a new stock. These species are usually graded up—that is, the available females, for instance, scrub cows or some low-producing stock of ewes, are fertilized by a bull or a ram of high quality. This is now more easily possible than it used to be because of the greatly improved technique of artificial insemination, as it is of course much cheaper and easier to transport the sperm from the breeding males over great distances than to transport the animals themselves, and a much greater number of females can be served than by the natural mating process. This latter advantage, however, differs greatly in the three species.

If the grading-up process is continued on the female offspring over several generations animals are obtained which are almost as good as the pure-bred stock and also breed fairly true. If the animals are living under hard conditions a graded-up stock may even be superior to the pure race in that particular environment.

Apart from grading up and from inbreeding, organized

cross-breeding is also widely used in animal husbandry. The mule, being a species cross between horse and donkey, and accordingly sterile, must of course perpetually be produced anew from the two parent species which are kept in separate breeds for this very purpose. Cross-breeding between strains of one species can have two advantages: in the first place, undesirable recessive characters are less likely to become manifest, and stronger animals often result from a cross than would be obtained from pure ancestral stocks, and, secondly, valuable economic characters of several breeds can be obtained in this way. In Australia, for instance, the hardiness, good fertility and the satisfactory milk supply of the ewe of some Merino stock are combined with the good mutton qualities from various rams, such as Border Leicester, Romney Marsh and Dorset Horn.

It seems to be generally agreed now that there is no such thing as an absolutely best variety of a plant or animal, but that different strains are best adapted to particular geographical regions. Some of the West European breeds of cattle which rank among the best milk producers in the world, do not do well in some tropical countries such as India and are sometimes even difficult to keep there. On the other hand, the native cattle of these regions, although they are very poor both in appearance and in milk production, are adapted to the local conditions, and yield a small but steady amount of milk. If milk production in these parts of the world is to be improved it is clearly not enough to introduce new livestock. It would appear to be much better to breed from the local cattle, with some addition from other breeds, and at the same time to improve the conditions under which the cattle have to live by providing water, salts and shade and by cultivating richer grass.

Similar simultaneous improvements in both genetic quality and environment should be aimed at in plant breeding.

Clearly a hardy crop which would do well on a poor soil in competition with numerous weeds will not necessarily give the best results in well-manured fields where the weeds are kept in hand. When there are climatic factors which cannot easily be changed, stocks must be bred which are suited to the particular circumstances; so, for example, the shortness of the summer in Canada used to put a very strict limit to the economic cultivation of wheat; early strains were easily damaged by the spring frosts and late strains could not mature quickly enough to ripen before the winter began. By a combination of genetical factors making for cold resistance on the one hand and for early development on the other, very good strains were bred—for example, 'Marquis'—and the belt of wheat production was pushed steadily farther north. A similar success was also achieved with the honey bee in Russia, where again cold was one of the limiting factors, whereas the other was the length of the bee's proboscis. Northern races of bees in Russia tended to have a short proboscis, while some of the most important nectar-producing flowers in this region—red clover, for instance—have rather long blossoms, so that the native bees could not get at the nectar at the bottom of the flowers. It has been claimed that by combining increased resistance to cold with a longer proboscis, strains have been obtained which can be kept much farther north than had been possible before.

CHAPTER XX

Human Genetics

HEREDITY in man must be studied by methods which are different from those used for animals and plants. People are never bred for experimental reasons, and a geneticist interesting himself in human heredity must collect his data from existing people and pedigrees; thus he will only infer by actuarial methods interrelationships that he could have obtained with certainty from a pre-arranged experiment. Other difficulties in studying human heredity are: (1) the longevity of man, which limits the number of generations that an investigator can observe at the same time to three or, at the most, four; (2) the low number of progeny; and (3) the high number of chromosomes ($2n = 48$) and the correspondingly high number of linkage groups. For these reasons elaborate statistical methods are needed in most fields of human genetics, but sometimes other methods are available.

There is, however, one favourable circumstance which proves quite useful in elucidating some facts of human heredity, and that is the existence of monozygotic twins. Two types of twins exist in man, binovular and uniovular, or dizygotic and monozygotic, and they occur in approximately equal numbers. Binovular twins originate from the fertilization of two separate ova by two separate sperms, and the children that develop from them are not more similar genetically than children of different ages from the same parents; for instance, they may be of different sex. In any case the chance that two brothers or two sisters get exactly the same two times twenty-four chromosomes in their chromosome make-up is represented by a number far exceeding the number of existing siblings. Monozygotic twins, on the other hand, originate by an accident happening during the earliest stages of cleavage, which results in the two halves of one fertilized egg developing independently into two complete individuals; therefore they are always of the same sex. One might say that such twins constitute a clóne. What actually happens is that the two cells which result from the first division of the fertilized egg do not keep together as they should, but get separated, and each starts developing independently. Such behaviour, which is abnormal in man and in most other animals, occurs normally in some species of parasitic wasps and also in a primitive mammal, the armadillo, where it is known as polyembryony. If the separation of the two halves is not complete double monsters are produced showing different degrees of separation; the famous Siamese twins resulted from an accident of this kind.

A comparison between monozygotic and dizygotic twins, or for that matter triplets or quadruplets, gives valuable information about the inheritance of human properties and faculties, and about the effects of genetical constitution as opposed to the effects of environment—that is, of nature as against nurture. Binovular twins of the same sex who grow up in the same family, with the same sort of education and social standing, are probably subjected to the most nearly uniform human environment conceivable; differences which they show will therefore be mainly due to genetical differences. Of course there will be differences which are clearly environmental in the lives of any pair of twins—for instance, one may die in a road accident or in war, which only serves to stress the fact that no two environments can be really identical. Monozygotic twins, on the other hand, may develop very peculiar and striking similarities even if they are brought up in quite different places, as may happen if they are adopted in childhood by different foster-parents. For instance, similar crimes have been perpetrated by monozygotic brothers living in different countries; or certain diseases, such as hay fever, asthma and tuberculosis, may start at approximately the same age and follow a very similar course in two widely separated monozygotic twins.

Twins of the same sex having a common placenta are always uniovular, but two placentæ do not exclude monozygosity. After birth this must be deduced from the finger-prints, similarities and dissimilarities in complexion, hair- and eye-colour, timbre of the voice, and so on. It is usually not very difficult to decide, and any twin brothers or sisters who are described as being as like as two peas can be safely taken to be monozygotic. The interpretation of psychological similarities in twins of both kinds needs some care, as the mere fact of being a twin may affect the mental development considerably. The tendency to produce twins, homozygotic or dizygotic, is itself inherited; in Europe about every eightieth birth produces twins.

Many of the inherited properties of man are controlled by numerous genes—for instance, the colour of eyes, hair and skin are all polygenic characters, and therefore a study of their heredity is very difficult. Many genetical rules which were laid down in the past before this was understood have since been disproved; it is not true, for example, that dark eye-colour is always dominant over light, and that therefore the children of two blue-eyed parents cannot have brown eyes, although it is true that it happens rarely. Similarly, red-haired parents usually have red-haired children, but not always. Some of the most interesting and important inborn characters in man are the diseases and defects both of body and of mind which are hereditary, but as their proper understanding needs considerable medical knowledge, only a few of them have been or will be mentioned. Hæmophilia, the Rhesus factor and colour-blindness are among them.

One of the striking features in human genetics is the apparent preponderance of dominant or semi-dominant genes, whereas most of the known genes in plants and animals are recessive, but this is really a consequence of the different methods applied in the two cases. If a plant or an animal species were studied simply by looking at numerous individuals, the dominants or semi-dominants would also be detected first, as they show when they are present in only one of two homologous chromosomes. If a gene making a normally red-eyed fly into a brown-eyed one could occur singly once in a thousand individuals it would occur doubly only once in a million, as will be understood from the penny-tossing experiments described in Chapter III, and, therefore, if it were dominant, it would be found in about ten individuals if 10,000 were investigated; but if it were recessive, probably not a single case would be found even in this number. The large number of recessive genes known in cultivated plants and animals is due to the amount of inbreeding that goes on in cultivation—an amount which is still further increased in breeding experiments, and which progressively increases the probability of two identical recessive genes meeting in one individual. As the amount of inbreeding in man is considerably less, and is steadily decreasing at present as a consequence of the breaking down of local barriers which used to restrict the movements of people, two identical recessive genes are much less likely to be united in one human individual, and therefore they will usually pass undetected. On the other hand, most of the rare recessive genes in man will be detected in communities which show a high degree of inbreeding—for instance, among the inhabitants of small islands or mountain valleys, or among members of religious minorities such as the Jews in Europe and the Parsees in India, or among groups which favour marriage between relatives, as happened in some of the

Egyptian dynasties. The possibly detrimental effect of the marriage of near relatives upon their progeny, which is due to the accumulation of unfavourable recessives, has always been realized by legislators and religious leaders from very early times, and therefore marriages between brothers and sisters, or even between uncles and nieces and aunts and nephews, are usually prohibited, and marriages between first cousins are often frowned upon. On the other hand, inbreeding may equally produce an increase in special gifts. Actually we frequently do not know what a human dominant looks like in the homozygous form; it may be lethal or may have a stronger effect than in the heterozygous form. For instance, one pedigree has been described where the brachyphalangous parents produced a child homozygous for this defect who had no arms, whereas the parents had only shorter fingers. There are two or three less clear cases.

Some of the inherited characters of man have a less serious aspect. Some people are able to roll up the sides of their tongues, and thus make the tongue into a sort of tube when they put it out; others cannot do this, and the difference seems to be largely due to a single genetical factor. Inherited differences also exist in tasting. There are people who can distinguish between a sugar solution and a saccharine solution, which to others appear identical. This is not necessarily an inherited ability, but in the following case the differences in tasting ability are inherited. A 0·05 per cent solution of an organic substance responsible for the bitter taste of grape-fruit rind, called phenyl-thio-urea or phenyl-thio-carbamide, can be tasted by some people, but not by others; most 'tasters' find it bitter and disagreeable, to others it tastes like pure water. The difference between people who can taste the solution and people who do not distinguish it from water is relatively clear-cut, and it is due to a single Mendelian gene, tasting being dominant. Whether a child tastes phenyl-thio-carbamide can be inferred from its facial expression at an early age; therefore 'tasting' can be used as evidence in cases of doubtful paternity.

It has been found that tasters and non-tasters also occur among chimpanzees, for by giving them solutions of phenyl-thio-urea to drink two sorts of behaviour can easily be recognized. Some of them show no disgust and excitement even if they drink repeatedly; others invariably make faces and spit, or even become violent. Thus it seems that the difference between tasters and non-tasters is a very old one which may have been preserved because it has no survival value. It has been shown that other inborn differences in human beings behave very similarly—for instance, the blood groups A and B.

CHAPTER XXI

Inherited Properties of Human Blood

THE great majority of human beings go through life paying very little attention to small cuts and bruises, but there are some boys and men who do not stop bleeding when they cut themselves, and who are also much more easily bruised than are other people. They have to be more careful in their physical activities than the normal run of mankind; taking out their first teeth may be a major operation owing to the bleeding which sometimes will not stop, and often their lives are saved only after many injections.

To understand what is wrong with such people one must consider the functions of the blood and of the blood vessels. Human blood circulates in a closed system of tubes, big ones leading from the heart, which are called arteries, and others leading to the heart, which are called veins; the arteries and veins are connected by numerous small tubes called capillaries. The effects of any injury to the circulatory system vary according to the place where the damage is done, but the loss of about one-fifth of one's blood endangers life. If the heart or any of the great arteries is punctured there is an imminent danger of death, for the blood pressure there is the greatest and the bleeding is the fastest; if smaller arteries, veins or capillaries are hurt most people's lives are not threatened, though sometimes even this may be dangerous.

The blood itself consists of the plasma, which is a pale yellow solution of many substances, and of the various corpuscles, either red or colourless, which are suspended in it. When any of the capillaries in a normal person is injured the wound bleeds for a little while, but if it is left alone the bleeding soon stops because the openings of the small blood vessels are filled with clotted blood. If blood is artificially prevented from clotting by adding sodium citrate to it, the corpuscles gradually sink to the bottom and the plasma remains as a clear solution on top. This clotting is an important function of the blood.

Clotting is dependent on many factors, among which are the presence of dissolved substances such as calcium, and of certain corpuscular elements—the thrombocytes. These break up when a vessel is damaged and release a substance into the blood, which in its turn transforms a protein dissolved in the plasma into an insoluble substance with a fibrous structure. The dissolved protein is called fibrinogen, while the insoluble one is called fibrin. Obviously blood must not clot inside the blood vessels, as it would block the circulation; but it is useful for it to clot when it is exposed to the air or when it comes into contact with injured tissues. If blood is deficient in any of the many constituents necessary for the formation of fibrin it will not clot, but the question which factor in the chain is lacking in the blood of people like the boys and men described is still a matter of controversy. Possibly it is a deficiency in the thrombocytes.

People whose blood shows insufficient powers of clotting are called hæmophiliacs (bleeders), and they are not distributed at random among the population. They are always boys or men, never girls or women, and they almost always belong to families where there are other boys and men who are to some extent similarly affected, though not all of them will be. The disease is due to a sex-linked recessive gene, and is therefore exhibited by men, but transmitted by women. A man who has hæmophilia may therefore have an apparently normal daughter, who may nevertheless transmit the condition to the grandchildren. Here again it will show if they are males, or be conducted still farther if they are females. Figure 23 shows the pedigree of a hæmophiliac family.

Loss of blood occurs most frequently in war-time, when many people are wounded, and therefore at a comparatively early date army surgeons tried to counteract heavy losses of blood. More than a hundred years ago experiments were made by injecting sheep's blood into human veins, and several lives were saved in this way; but as numerous accidents also occurred, the practice was given up. Later on solutions of various salts were tried, with varying degrees of

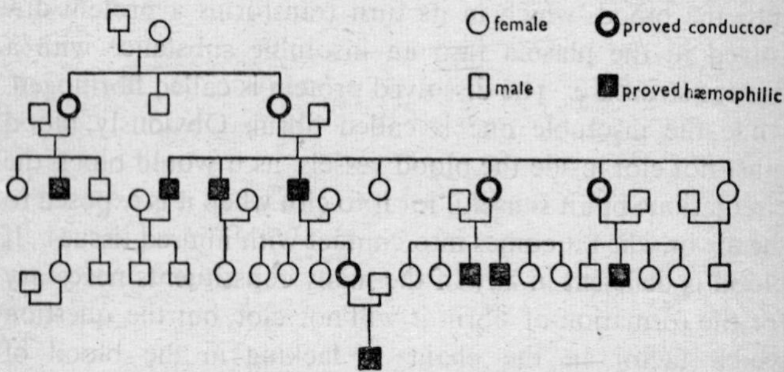

FIG. 23.—Pedigree of a hæmophilic family showing inheritance of a recessive sex-linked character. (From Birch, Hæmophilia, Urbana 1937).

success, the most famous one being devised by an English physiologist named Ringer; but blood seemed to be more desirable, and so transfusions of blood from one man to another were tried as soon as an apparatus could be constructed which prevented the blood of the donor from clotting. Many more lives were saved by this method than by the transfusion of sheep's blood, but there were still a number of fatal accidents. The explanation of these was given by an Austrian called Landsteiner, who detected that the blood of any one man can be safely injected into the veins of some people without ill effect, whereas it causes serious disturbance when injected into the veins of others. By mixing drops of blood, which had been prevented from clotting by chemical means, he observed that different effects were obtained according to the people from whom the drops came—that is to say, that everybody's blood does not of necessity behave in the same way.

If drops of plasma from one man are mixed with drops of blood from a number of others sometimes clumping occurs and sometimes it does not. If, now, plasma from one of the people whose corpuscles clumped is mixed with drops of blood from the same set of people, including the original donor, most of the people whose corpuscles did not clump with the first man's plasma will clump now, and vice versa. People exist, however, whose corpuscles never clump with any serum, and there are others whose corpuscles clump almost invariably. It is simpler to give the results of Landsteiner's experiments rather than to explain the roundabout way in which he obtained them.

The behaviour of the blood and the inheritance of the blood groups can be explained by assuming that there are three alleles, A, B and O, occurring in one locus of an autosome in such a way that only two of them can be combined in one individual. In addition, it appears that the serological properties dependent on the presence of A or B are independent of each other, so that an individual carrying A and B will react to both sera and will not react intermediately.

The following table shows the distribution of antibodies in the serum and antigens in the red blood cells in the different blood groups:

Antigens in red cells	O	A	B	A–B
Antibodies in serum	Anti-A + Anti-B	Anti-B	Anti-A	None

The relative frequency of the different blood groups can be deduced from their distribution in a big sample of the population in the way indicated in the chapter on the Spreading of Genes in Populations. The factors which determine to which of the four blood groups a human being belongs are not evenly distributed throughout the people of the world; the factor A is more commonly found in the west of Europe than in the east, while the factor B shows the opposite state of affairs, though it is always less common than A. By determining the relative proportion of these two factors it is possible sometimes to get information about the mixing of peoples and their migrations in the past, and even in prehistoric times. We do not know how these distributions originated, but, as it is unlikely that it makes a great difference to human beings to which blood group they belong, one would be inclined to assume that the different alleles that determine the groups have originated in different regions of the earth and have spread from their places of origin; alternatively, one could assume local differences in mutation rate. The great gradients mentioned above can be considered as the consequence of the slow diffusion of one allele through intermarriage between neighbouring populations; where communities which inbreed to a certain extent have migrated one would expect that they would show a blood group distribution intermediate between that of their present neighbours and that of the inhabitants of their former home. Actually Jewish and gypsy populations in Central Europe do show slightly higher percentages of the factor B than the other inhabitants of the same localities, but lower percentages of B than many of the non-Jewish and non-gypsy populations farther east. Of the Blackfoot Indians of America, on the other hand, 80 per cent belong to group A, and their most conspicuous feature is complete absence of B; it is now assumed that B has originated by mutation in the Old World.

The result of testing blood groups is now frequently admitted as evidence in courts of law in cases of doubtful paternity. If the mother, child and possible fathers submit to the test it can sometimes be stated that such-and-such a man cannot be the father of a given child; but the blood group can never be used to prove paternity. The following table gives the possible blood groups of children which may result from any given pair of parents:

GROUPS OF PARENTS	POSSIBLE GROUPS OF CHILDREN
O × O	O
O × A	O, A
O × B	O, B
A × A	O, A
A × B	O, A, B
B × B	O, B
A × AB	A, B, AB
B × AB	A, B, AB
AB × AB	A, B, AB

There are other factors known by which human blood corpuscles and serum differ which have nothing to do with the groups O, A, B and AB; two are called *M* and *N*, and they are alleles inherited independently of A and B. The factors *M* and *N* were found by differences in the reaction of rabbit serum after rabbits had been injected with blood from different people.

Recently a factor known as Rh has been described. This was discovered originally as the result of an experiment in which the blood of a Rhesus monkey was injected into a rabbit. The rabbit responded by producing in its serum an anti-Rhesus body which had the property of clumping a suspension of the red blood cells of the Rhesus monkey. It was then found that this antibody also caused the clumping of the red cells of 85 per cent of white people, who are therefore called Rh positive, while in 15 per cent cells did not clump, and these are called Rh negative.

Under certain circumstances Rh-negative human beings can behave in the same way as the rabbit. If an Rh-negative patient is transfused with Rh-positive blood he may make the anti-Rh body in his serum. If this happens and more Rh positive blood is subsequently transfused it may be destroyed just as if it were incompatible with the ABO grouping already mentioned. This destruction of the Rh positive transfused cells may prove fatal.

Again, if an Rh-negative woman is carrying an Rh-positive fœtus, the Rh-positive gene having been inherited from the father, she may be stimulated by the fœtal red cells to produce anti-Rh body. This fortunately occurs only in about one-twentieth of pregnancies where the Rh groups make it a possibility, for about one-tenth of all pregnancies are of this type. Such immunization, as it is called, has no obvious effect on the mother, but the Rh antibody damages the fœtal red cells, and the baby may be stillborn or suffer from severe anæmia and jaundice if it is born alive. The discovery of the cause of this type of anæmia resulted in a great step forward in treatment, and nowadays the baby is given transfusions of Rh-negative blood.

CHAPTER XXII

Eugenics, Negative and Positive

MOST people agree that human affairs are seldom in a satisfactory state, and there is a general tendency to try to improve them. This can be done in various ways; but the improvements desired by different people are themselves very different. Whatever the ideals may be in accordance with which one wants to change both human individuals and their community, it is important to know which human properties are inherited and which are environmentally conditioned, or, better still, how heredity and environment interact in producing manifest qualities. These, it will be remembered, were the deliberations from which a start was made at the beginning of this book. Unfortunately it is rarely possible to assess completely what is due to nature and what is due to nurture in human relationships; and least so when the question is most urgent. In South Africa, for example, an assumed innate inferiority of the native population is taken as the basis for increasing the degree of racial segregation. When the state of affairs mentioned in 'Africa Report' in 1938 is realized, it becomes difficult to see how intellectual equality between blacks and whites could be expected; in Northern Rhodesia, for example, £28 8*s*. 7*d*. a head annually is stated to have been paid by the Government for the education of a white child, and only 4*s*. 6*d*. for that of a native child. It has frequently been claimed that the mixed offspring of white and Negro parents, or indeed of any other mixture where the parents come from widely different stocks, are inferior to both parental stocks, although this has never really been proved, and certainly not by measuring specific properties, such as intelligence or social worth. All that can be said with certainty is that under conditions where one or both of the parental stocks resent the mixture a mixed class will often be victimized, and will then be forced to live in a less good environment than either of the original stocks. This is especially the case when there are only a few people in this position, as they may not be able to develop a social life of their own. On the other hand, isolated individuals of mixed origin may not be discriminated against at all. Unfortunately no one has so far collected the history of all the colour bars in the world, although a comparison of all the conditions and the complete facts would be most illuminating. But the information available shows that there are some mixed populations of quite recent origin where hardly any racial discrimination exists—for instance, in Hawaii and Cuba, and also perhaps in some of the South American Republics. It seems that the people in these communities are quite efficient, and probably very much happier than those living under the rigid colonial system. Mixtures of populations which are less distinct certainly do not decrease the vitality of the individuals or their social faculties, as the English and the North American populations amply demonstrate.

The study of the histories of the individual colour bars shows that where a bar is found it is always bound up with a class difference, such as the difference between conquerors and conquered, or between the full citizen and the immigrants. The North American Negroes, for example, are all descended from slaves, and they are still widely regarded as inferiors. This has also influenced the status of the natives in Africa. The Jews were debarred in many European countries from owning land or from military and civil service, and the status of a Jew was again considered inferior. However, almost everywhere there are more or less distinct classes of people who do not differ in their pigmentation or in other obvious anatomical details, and between whom genetical differences are entirely unknown. The views which various people take on the origin or the desirability of class differences greatly influence their opinions on the part played in class formation by heredity. People of high social standing, especially when this is due to inherited money, often like to justify their acceptance of privileges by asserting that they are racially superior and that a child of the lower classes would not as a rule develop into such a fine specimen, or be able to make such good use of his privileges. The dispossessed, on the other hand, will be very much inclined to deny that there are inherited merits in his social superiors, but will attribute any merits there may be either to what he calls the chance of social standing or, perhaps with more justification, to markedly undesirable properties. Both radical attitudes are not supported by the facts. So long as a social system of some stability is not too rigid a certain rise of the more gifted and a certain fall of the less gifted are almost certain to happen, but as such changes are rather slow, unequal distribution of inborn qualities among the classes will always persist.

Some people think this natural movement in the population is sufficient at present to counteract violent political tension, whereas others think that the present social structure of Western peoples must unavoidably lead not only to a decrease in their numbers, but to the loss of the more gifted by the operation of a selective birth rate. Both statements are too vague to be wholly true. Their greatest defect is that their exponents tend to apply their criteria to the individual instead of to the individual in his relation to the social structure. For instance, an aggressive or acquisitive person will be very valuable in an expanding society where there is a struggle with nature; but in an over-populated and civilized country such people must of necessity prey upon their fellow-men, and cannot be regarded as desirable. A further complication is that in human society it is not only the individuals that are subject to selection, but that selection also operates upon whole groups which are not always composed of related individuals, or even of individuals of similar genetical composition. It would appear that most amateur eugenists are dealing with a cloud-cuckoo-land and not with reality, and they tend especially to be guilty of neglecting economic factors. Nevertheless several limited fields remain where eugenics may prove useful. First, the quantitative development of the population must be investigated, and attempts can be made to adjust propagation to the needs and possibilities of future generations. In a stable or slowly increasing people there should always be a certain proportion of producing members and non-producing members, the latter being children, old people and the sick. If the birth rate suddenly drops, the growing generation has to carry too heavy a burden of non-producers. On the other hand, sudden and artificial increases in child-bearing can never be maintained unless they are accompanied by marked changes in the construction of the society—that is, in the way in which the people earn their living. Another important quantitative problem is the maintenance of an approximately normal sex ratio. This may be greatly disturbed by modern war, and since our monogamous society is difficult to adjust in this respect, it should perhaps avoid wars.

Qualitative eugenics can be subdivided into negative and positive. Attempts to prevent the birth of very unfit children and to discourage the propagation of less desirable members of the community have unfortunately become attached to political issues, and it is difficult to discuss these without rousing immediate controversy, but several points will have become clear from this book. Firstly, hereditary abnormalities, such as insanity or permanent sickness, which incapacitate an individual so much that he becomes a permanent burden on society, are none too frequent. Secondly, it is usually only a possibility and not a certainty that such a deficiency will be handed on to the children of a particular couple. Thirdly, most of the graver abnormalities prevent their carriers from propagation, and thus make eugenic measures unnecessary. Fourthly, the breaking down of mating barriers in modern times decreases the likelihood of two recessives being joined in one individual. In addition, if such a gene were present at the rate of 1 per 1,000 in a population, homozygotes showing its effects would only occur with a frequency of one in a million; obviously the elimination of such a person would still leave the 999 heterozygotes to spread the gene. The only conclusion to be drawn from this is that intermarriage between relatives should be discouraged when there is a likelihood of two harmful recessives meeting in their offspring. Therefore in most cases drastic measures, such as sterilization, and especially enforced sterilization, cannot be supported by geneticists, except possibly in the case of certain rare mental defects and of some gross anatomical defects in which the mode of transmission has been fully investigated. Instead of relying upon legislative measures, genetical knowledge and sound views on human qualities should be spread.

Even less can be said for positive eugenics. Even if it were desirable to produce more geniuses, whatever that may mean, there is no recipe for their production at present. Peculiar qualities which make for human greatness are probably due to the mixture of many genes and develop only in particular circumstances, which may be called congenial, but are at present impossible to define. However, special traits, such as musical gifts (Figure 24), or mathematical ability, or a capacity to paint, are largely due to inherited factors, and if one considers them as particularly desirable one may choose one's mate accordingly.

On the whole it must be said that the less people understand of heredity the more they try to explain by it in politics

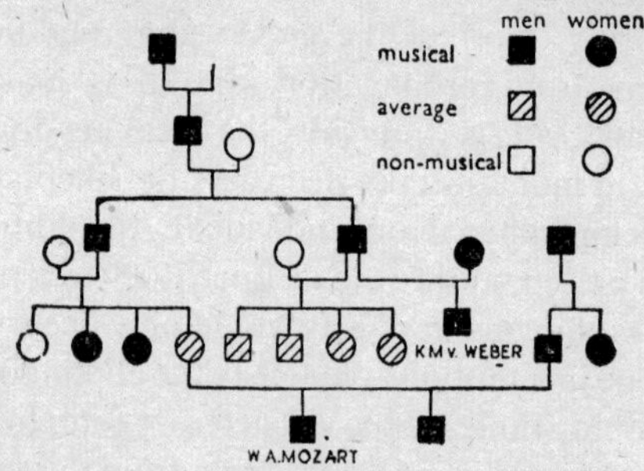

FIG. 24.—Distribution of musical ability in the Mozart–Weber family.

and social life. A true eugenic programme will have to find a balance between the improvement of the conditions of human life and the selection of the inborn qualities of mankind.

CHAPTER XXIII

Some Genetical and Statistical Fallacies

IN the course of its progress science not only discovers new facts and develops new concepts, but by doing so it destroys old opinions, and especially prescientific superstitions. As many of these die hard, especially when they concern human biology, some of the less obvious fallacies are listed below.

A very suggestive trap into which quite famous people have fallen is the following. Many people deplore the extinction of talent by the operation of the differential propagation rate which is characteristic of our society. It is possible that they are right, but the following argument, which is frequently heard in this connection, is certainly fallacious. It has been argued that famous musicians, or for that matter painters, always produce less offspring than their parents, and statistics seem to bear this out; the interpretation given was that musicians or painters are less fertile than the rest of the population. But a curious selection of the material has been overlooked in the argument—namely, that the parents of the artists were not comparable to the artists themselves, since they are selected as parents, which means that possible progenitors of gifted artists who for some reason had no children were left out. In short, while the offspring must have had parents, their contemporaries need not have had offspring. So there may have been as many childless people in the parent generation as in the artist's generation. This example serves to show that common sense as usually understood does not always produce valid conclusions, and that statistics prove very little unless it is clearly understood what they are dealing with.

The alleged inherent inferiority of half-castes as well as of the lower classes has already been discussed. In its support it has often been stated that hybrids from widely differing breeds of dogs are often deformed, and sometimes not fertile, or even not viable. The analogy, however, is not a sound one. In the first place breeds in dogs are not adaptations to natural conditions, but are usually products of fancy breeding, and are often already biologically unbalanced, especially so far as their endocrines are concerned. Secondly, the differences in such characters as size, hairiness and form of skeleton (skull and pelvis) that are found in the various breeds are infinitely greater than those found in the human races, where in numerous mixed populations no signs of incompatibility in mating have been observed.

The belief that two blue-eyed parents cannot produce a brown-eyed child has cast doubts on the legitimacy of many children in the past. Although, as we have seen, this rule usually applies, it is not invariably true, because light and dark eye-colours are not determined by single Mendelian pairs, but by a number of genes.

A rather curious phenomenon which shows the intricacy of statistical methods is the observed numerical deficiency of children under five years old. American sociologists have found out that in a well-defined area there frequently appeared to be more children of 10–15 years than there had been children of 0–5 years ten years previously. This paradoxical situation remained unchanged when allowance was made for death and migration, but the riddle was solved by individual enquiry—people had forgotten the baby when the census man came.

In genetical experiments most use is made of organisms producing a fair number of offspring. Unfortunately man never belonged to this category, and especially nowadays most families in the Western countries are small, so the genetical evidence must often be collected from observations made on many families lumped together. By this method unexpected deviations from the ordinary Mendelian ratios were frequently noticed which puzzled many investigators. The following considerations show that there are factors which decrease the apparent frequency of recessives and others which increase it. For instance, if most of the families investigated consist of two or three children and are selected because one of the children shows a certain defect, all the families where no homozygous recessive child has been produced will escape detection and will not enter into the material. If in such a family both parents are heterozygous for an autosomal recessive, the probability that neither of the two children will share it is $\frac{9}{16}$ths, which means that more than half of the families of this class will escape detection. Consequently in material derived from small families where the defect appears the incidence of a mutant of this type will always be much more than $\frac{1}{4}$. On the other hand, the greater mortality of many homozygotes will decrease their frequency in any census, and therefore in circumstances other than those just described less than $\frac{1}{4}$ mutants may be found in the course of an investigation.

Although the pre-genetical sex theories have been definitely superseded by the Mendelian theory given in this book, they are still widely believed, and new ones are invented every year; but they are so contradictory that anybody who has any knowledge of genetics will not take them seriously.

Another widespread superstition is that congenital diseases are synonymous with hereditary diseases. There is no such thing as hereditary syphilis or tuberculosis; there may be some hereditary predisposition for tuberculosis, but this disease does not develop without massive infection, and if a new-born baby has syphilis it is because it has been handed over from the mother to the fœtus as an infectious disease.

Horse-breeders and genealogists frequently maintain that a mare can be spoilt by a bad stallion as far as later matings are concerned, and that noble blood can also be contaminated in this way by misalliances. The mechanism of heredity as explained in this book leaves no place for such assumptions. What may happen is that a female organism may be damaged by its sexual partner by way of infection or, more rarely still, by way of sensitization. It has already been mentioned that the formation of antibodies against Rh blood factors occurring in a fœtus of a woman not showing this factor is responsible for a certain proportion of miscarriages, and cases of severe jaundice of the newborn.

One of the worst superstitions, and one which has probably been doing much damage, is the idea of degeneracy, a sort of all-round decay of mythical racial qualities, which is held responsible for the biological and political downfall of families and nations. There is no reason to believe that such catastrophes ever happen. The downfall of families, classes and nations is very rarely due to genetical deterioration, but mostly to a deterioration of the conditions in which the children are brought up and in which the adults have to live.

A related fallacy bears the name anticipation. Many doctors believe that some hereditary diseases, such as cataract and a progressive degeneration of muscles (myotonia) show an earlier onset and greater severity in the successive generations of a family and thus lead to its extinction. Many pedigrees have been published in support of this hypothesis, but the statistics can be explained by a complicated bias in sampling, without any real biological basis.

Logical thought, combined with even as little knowledge

as a book like this may impart, ought to be a help in the detection of some of the contradictions and fabrications in the field of human genetics which racial propaganda and counter-propaganda have very successfully spread all over the earth.

Some Important Books and Periodicals

DEALING WITH GENETICS AND RELATED SUBJECTS

BOOKS

BABCOCK, E. B., and CLAUSEN, R. E. *Genetics in Relation to Agriculture*. 1927. New York

BATESON, W. *Mendel's Principles of Heredity*. 1930. Cambridge

COCKAYNE, E. A. *Inherited Abnormalities of the Skin and its Appendages*. 1933. Oxford

CRANE, M. B., and LAWRENCE, W. J. C. *The Genetics of Garden Plants*. 1936. London

DARLINGTON, C. D. *Recent Advances in Cytology*. 1937. London

DAVENPORT, C. R., and STEGGERDA, M. *Race-Crossing in Jamaica*. 1929. Carnegie Inst.

DOBZHANSKY, T. *Genetics and the Origin of Species*. 1942. Columbia Univ. Press

FISHER, R. A. *The Genetical Theory of Natural Selection*. 1938. Oxford

GATES, R. R. *Human Genetics*. 2 vols. 1946. New York

GOLDSCHMIDT, R. *Physiological Genetics*. 1938. New York

HALDANE, J. B. S. *The Causes of Evolution*. 1932. London.
Heredity and Politics. 1938. London
New Paths in Genetics. 1941. London

HUXLEY, J. S. *Evolution, the Modern Synthesis*. 1942. London

MOHR, O. *Heredity and Disease*. 1934. New York

MORANT, G. M. *The Races of Central Europe*. 1939. London

MORGAN, T. H. *The Theory of the Gene*. 1926. New Haven

NEWMAN, H. H. *Twins and Supertwins*. 1944. Chicago

SINNOTT, E. W., and DUNN, L. C. *Principles of Genetics*. 1939. New York

SNYDER, L. H. *The Principles of Heredity*. 2nd ed. 1940. New York

STERN, CURT. *Principles of Human Genetics*. 1949. Freeman and Co., San Francisco

STURTEVANT, A. H., and BEADLE, G. W. *Introduction to Genetics*. 1940

Treasury of Human Inheritance. Since 1912. London

WADDINGTON, C. H. *Introduction to Modern Genetics*. 1939. London

WHITE, M. J. D. *The Chromosomes*. 1937. London

Animal Cytology and Evolution. 1945. Cambridge

WRIEDT, CHR. *Heredity in Livestock*. 1931. London

JOURNALS

Animal Breeding Abstracts
Annals of Eugenics
Eugenics Review
Journal of Genetics
American Naturalist
The American Journal of Human Genetics
Journal of Heredity
Genetica
Hereditas
Zeitschrift für Induktive Abstammungs- und Vererbungslehre

Glossary

OF SOME GENETICAL, CYTOLOGICAL AND RELATED TERMS

Allelomorphs: different genes occupying the same place (locus) in homologous chromosomes

Allelomorphs, multiple: more than two allelomorphs occupying the same place

Allopolyploid: a fertile hybrid having two or more haploid sets of chromosomes from each parent

Alternation of generations: regular alternation between sexual and asexual propagation

Apogamy: generation by an unpollinated ovum

Autopolyploid: having multiple chromosome sets of the same species

Autosome: chromosome other than sex chromosome

Back-cross: crossing of a hybrid to one of the parental stocks

Biometry: application of measurement to living beings

Centromere: organ in the chromosome by which it is attached to the spindle

Centrosome: structure appearing in animal cells at the poles of the spindle during cell division, forming head of spermatozoon

Chiasma: visible exchange of homologous segments between two out of four chromatids during meiosis

Chloroplasts: green bodies enclosed in plant cells

Chromatid: split half of a chromosome

Chromatin: substance occupying the regions in a chromosome which are stained by certain dyes

Chromomere: smallest morphologically distinguishable part of a chromosome

Chromosomes: permanent structures in the cell nucleus staining with certain dyes and carrying the genes in linear arrangement

Clone: population of organisms derived from a common ancestor by mitotic divisions without chromosome re-arrangements

Coupling: phase of linkage when the recessive or the dominant allelomorphs of two linked genes are in one chromosome

Crossing over: genetical consequences of chiasma formation; the exchange of homologous segments of chromatids

Cytoplasm: content of cell body as distinct from the nucleus

Diploid: carrying two homologous sets of chromosomes

Dominant: a genetical character showing in the heterozygote

Enzymes: catalysts speeding up chemical reactions

Expressivity: degree of manifestation of a mutant gene in an individual

Gametophyte: stage in higher plants producing ova or sperms

Genes: material units of heredity, capable of reproduction and mutation, linearly arranged in the chromosomes

Genotype: the total gene complement in an individual

Gynandromorph: pathological individual composed of male and female parts

Haemophilia: sex-linked hereditary defect preventing blood from clotting normally

Haploid: carrying only one set of chromosomes

Heterogametic sex: sex in which there are both male and female producing gametes

Homozygous: possessing one or more equal pairs of alleles

Hormone: substance secreted by a ductless gland affecting other organs of the body by way of the body fluids

Identical twins: two individuals developing from the same fertilized egg

Inversion: change in position of a segment of a chromosome inverting the order of the genes

Lethal: mutant causing death at an early stage

Linkage group: genes situated in the same chromosome and therefore jointly transmitted except for crossing over

Locus: position occupied by a gene in a chromosome

Meiosis: reduction of chromosome number brought about by two consecutive nuclear divisions often involving pairing of homologous chromosomes and crossing over

Mitosis: cell division involving longitudinal splitting of the chromosomes and their equal distribution to the daughter cells

Monozygotic: originating from a single fertilized egg

Multiple factors: non-allelic genes affecting the same visible character

Mutant: carrier of a mutation

Mutation: sudden change in a gene which is permanently transmitted to the offspring

Normal distribution: a type of symmetrical curve or distribution of variations

Nucleolus: body of nucleo-proteins periodically produced by a chromosome

Nucleus: cell organ necessary for division, composed of the chromosomes, the nuclear sap and a membrane

Ovum: unfertilized egg

Parthenogenesis: propagation without male, with or without meiosis

Penetrance: percentage manifestations of a mutation in a progeny

Phenotype: external appearance of an organism resulting from the interaction of its genotype and its environment

Pleiotropy: manifold manifestation of a single mutant gene

Polymorphism: occurrence of different forms in one species

Polyploid: carrying more than two sets of chromosomes

Repulsion: phase of linkage where the recessive allelomorph of a gene is in the same chromosome as the dominant of a second gene

Sporophyte: diploid generation in mosses and ferns carrying spores corresponding to the vegetative part of a flowering plant

Tetrads: four cells derived from a mother cell by meiosis

Tetraploid: possessing four sets of chromosomes

Translocation: change in position of part of a chromosome to another non-homologous chromosome

Triploid: possessing three sets of chromosomes

Vegetative reproduction: reproduction not involving meiosis, *e.g.*, by tubers, cuttings, runners, etc.

Zygote: product of the union of two gametes, *e.g.*, ovum and sperm

Index

ALSO PUBLISHED AS A PELICAN

THE PHYSICAL BASIS OF PERSONALITY

V. H. Mottram

A 139

Personality is conditioned by two main factors – environment and heredity. It is with the second of these that this book is mainly concerned. Attempting to bridge the gap between the biological and the theological viewpoints regarding the reasons for the uniqueness of the individual, it discusses and explains in non-technical language the mechanism of physical inheritance in the living cell, the arrangement and behaviour of the chromosomes, sex determination, Mendelian inheritance and its laws in plants, animals and man, the constitution and working of the sympathetic and parasympathetic systems and their influence on individuality, and the part played by the endocrine organs in personal make-up. The few technical terms used are carefully explained in a glossary compiled specially for the reader who approaches the subject for the first time.

A brilliant description of genes, glands, chromosomes, all the physical causes which go so far to shape personality. ... Millions of wasted words since Darwinism struck the gong for the fight between Science and Religion would have been saved if this kind of approach had been made oftener from both sides of the great divide. – John o'London's Weekly.

ONE SHILLING AND SIXPENCE

PHYSIOLOGY AND PSYCHOLOGY

HUMAN PHYSIOLOGY

Kenneth Walker

A 102

A simple explanation of how the body works, not only in disease, but when functioning normally and healthily.

THE PHYSIOLOGY OF SEX

Kenneth Walker

A 71

A straightforward statement of the facts of sex and its problems in the life of the individual and the community.

GROW UP – AND LIVE

Eustace Chesser

A 149

A book to help boys and girls to accommodate themselves to the world in which they are growing up.

THE PERSONALITY OF MAN

G. N. M. Tyrrell

A 165

An explanation of the present position of psychical research, and a summary of the results it has so far gained.

MAN THE UNKNOWN

Alexis Carrel

A 181

A synthesis of what the various sciences have discovered about the nature of man, including a vigorous advocacy of the natural laws man must follow to be redeemed from the degeneracy of industrial civilisation.

ONE SHILLING AND SIXPENCE

PHILOSOPHY AND BELIEF

MEANING AND PURPOSE

Kenneth Walker

A211

An analysis of the main scientific theories of the last hundred years and their impact upon religious thought and belief.

BEFORE PHILOSOPHY

H. and H. A. Frankfort, J. Wilson and T. Jacobsen

A198

An analysis of the myths which for Ancient Man represented his peculiar form of concrete thought concerning the problems of self and the universe, his moral and religious preoccupations.

RELIGION AND THE RISE OF CAPITALISM

R. H. Tawney

A32

A study of religious thought on social issues during the three centuries from the later middle ages to the early eighteenth century.

ADVENTURES OF IDEAS *

A. N. Whitehead

A103

A history of the human race in terms of its mental experience through the centuries. In the author's words 'a study of the concept of civilization and an endeavour to understand how it is that civilized beings arise.'

COMPARATIVE RELIGION †

A. C. Bouquet

A89

A survey and comparison of the great religions of the world, and an examination of their significance to-day.

ONE SHILLING AND SIXPENCE EACH

* TWO SHILLINGS † TWO SHILLINGS AND SIXPENCE

SCIENCE

ATOMIC ENERGY

Edited by Dr J. L. Crammer and Professor R. E. Peierls, F.R.S.

A 224

Has atomic energy any peaceful uses? Where is uranium found? What are the risks to health from the radiation given out by decomposing atomic nuclei? The answers to these and other questions are outlined by a group of British and American scientists, who describe the processes by which atomic bombs are produced and discuss the constructive uses of atomic energy.

THE SCIENCE OF FLIGHT

Professor O. G. Sutton, F.R.S.

A 209

A simple and mainly non-technical account of aerodynamics, the science of which lies at the root of the problem of mechanical flight from the earliest projectiles to the rocket and the jet-propelled aeroplane. With eight illustrations and many diagrams.

THE SCIENTIFIC ATTITUDE

Professor C. H. Waddington, F.R.S.

A 84

'This is an important book, because it is, so far as I know, the first intelligent and intelligible attempt to associate the attitude of science with the attitude of art; to integrate the approach of factual and controlled observation with the approach of intuition and inspiration.' – Tom Harrison in the *New Statesman.*

THE INVENTOR AND HIS WORLD

Dr H. Stafford Hatfield

A 178

Inventors of genius are more valuable to-day than ever before. This book, which is a survey of the whole field of invention, is addressed to such men to explain them to themselves, and also to the public at large, who, finding them difficult, are often unhelpful and minimize the importance of their work.

ONE SHILLING AND SIXPENCE EACH

PELICAN BOOKS

A179

GENETICS

H. KALMUS

AND

LETTICE M. CRUMP